# Harold R Foster

# Prince Valiant

**COMPRISING PAGES 231 THROUGH 276**

# Journey To Africa

FANTAGRAPHICS BOOKS

## ABOUT THIS EDITION:

Produced in cooperation with the Danish publisher Interpresse and several other publishers around the world, this new edition of *PRINCE VALIANT* is intended to be the definitive compilation of Hal Foster's masterpiece.

In addition to this volume, Fantagraphics Books has in stock eight more collections of Foster's *Prince Valiant* work (Vols. 1-5, 29-31). Future releases will continue reprinting the earlier material (from 1942 through the end of the 1950s); once the series has "caught up" with its earlier releases, those will be reprinted, or (if they are still in print) skipped in order to complete the collection with the final era (late 1960s through 1982, when Foster handed over the strip to John Cullen Murphy). The ultimate goal is to have all 40 volumes in print simultaneously, making available the entirety of Hal Foster's 45-year epic.

## ABOUT THE PUBLISHER:

FANTAGRAPHICS BOOKS has dedicated itself to bringing readers the finest in comic book and comic strip material, both new and old. Its "classics" division includes the multi-volume *Complete E.C. Segar Popeye*, several volumes of *Little Orphan Annie* reprints, and the magazine *NEMO: The Classic Comics Library*. Its "modern" division is responsible for such works as Yellow Kid Award-winner *Love and Rockets* by Los Bros. Hernandez, Peter Bagge's *Neat Stuff*, the American edition of Munoz and Sampayo's *Sinner*, and *The Complete Crumb Comics*. See the back cover for a complete listing.

## PREVIOUS VOLUMES IN THIS SERIES:

PRINCE VALIANT, Volume 6
"Journey to Africa"
comprising pages 231 (July 13, 1941) through 276 (May 24, 1942)
Published by Fantagraphics Books, 1800 Bridgegate Street Suite 101, Westlake Village, CA 91361
Editorial Co-Ordinator: Helle Nielsen
Colored by Montse Serra of Bardon Art, S.A.
Cover inked by Gorm Transgaard and colored by Sussi Bech
Fantagraphics Books staff: Kim & Mark Thompson
Copyright © 1989 King Features Syndicate, Inc., Bull's, Interpresse, and Fantagraphics Books, Inc.
Printed in Italy
ISBN 0-930193-77-6
First printing: Spring, 1989

**Synopsis:** THE DUEL BETWEEN ANGOR WRACK AND PRINCE VALIANT IS **NEVER** FINISHED, BUT ENDS IN CAPTURE BY THE DRUSES, AN ARAB TRIBE WHOSE HATRED VAL HAS EARNED. THE STORY OF THEIR ESCAPE HAS BEEN TOLD AND NOW VAL HOLDS THE PASS, WHILE THE WOUNDED ANGOR WRACK ESCAPES.

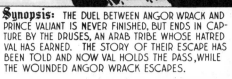

STEALTHILY THE NIMBLE ARABS ENCIRCLE THE MENACING FIGURE IN THE CLEFT.

THE PAIN OF HIS WOUNDS IS NOTHING COMPARED TO THE ANGUISH IN THE BOLD HEART OF ANGOR WRACK, AS HE RIDES TO SAFETY, LEAVING HIS MORTAL ENEMY TO BATTLE ALONE.

THEY COULD HAVE KILLED HIM WITH A FLIGHT OF SWIFT ARROWS, BUT THEY WANT HIM ALIVE, AND VAL IS MAKING IT VERY DIFFICULT.

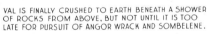

VAL IS FINALLY CRUSHED TO EARTH BENEATH A SHOWER OF ROCKS FROM ABOVE, BUT NOT UNTIL IT IS TOO LATE FOR PURSUIT OF ANGOR WRACK AND SOMBELENE.

WHEN NEXT VAL OPENS HIS EYES THE ARAB CHIEFTAIN IS BENDING OVER HIM. "*I AM THE ONE WHOSE SLAVES YOU TOOK, YOUR JEWELED SWORD WILL REPAY MY LOSS AND YOU WILL BE SOLD INTO SLAVERY.*" VAL DOES NOT UNDERSTAND THE WORDS, BUT THE EXPRESSIVE HANDS TELL HIM WHAT IS MEANT.

FOR MANY WEARY DAYS HE LIES SECURELY CHAINED IN A WELL-GUARDED TENT, WHILE HIS CRACKED BONES HEAL.

THEN, ONE EVENING HE IS PUT UPON A MOUNT AND TAKEN TO DAMASCUS.

AND THERE, IN THE SLAVE MARKET, HE IS OFFERED FOR SALE.
NEXT WEEK — **Sold.**

**Synopsis:** ONCE PRINCE VALIANT WHIPPED SOME ARAB SLAVE-DEALERS AND FREED THEIR WRETCHED MERCHANDISE. THEN THE WHEEL OF FORTUNE TURNED AND NOW THE SAME ARABS ARE SELLING BOTH VAL AND THE "SINGING SWORD" IN THE DAMASCUS BAZAAR.

SUCH A STRONG, YOUNG BODY SHOULD BRING A GOOD PRICE, THINK THE ARABS, AS THEIR VICTIM IS PLACED ON THE BLOCK IN THE SLAVE MARKET     BUT ONE LOOK AT HIS BLAZING EYES AND SET FACE DISCOURAGES WOULD-BE PURCHASERS......

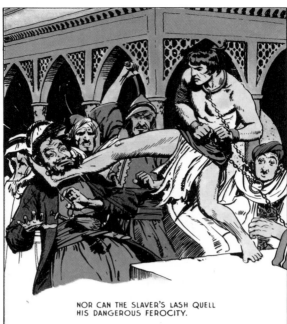

NOR CAN THE SLAVER'S LASH QUELL HIS DANGEROUS FEROCITY.

A RICH MERCHANT STROLLS TOWARD THE BLOCK. VAL STARES, FOR HANGING OVER THE BUYER'S BULGING STOMACH IS THE NEWLY-PURCHASED "SINGING SWORD."

NOW A GREAT CHANGE COMES OVER VAL. HE STANDS MEEK AND MILD, LIKE A GOOD SLAVE, WHILE THE AMAZED SLAVE-DEALER ACCEPTS THE MERCHANT'S FIRST BID.... GLAD TO BE RID OF THE HUMAN TIGER.

FOR VAL WANTS TO FOLLOW THE "SWORD," AND HE DOES, AS A SLAVE, ACROSS THREE HUNDRED MILES OF SYRIAN DESERT.

A MONTH LATER THE WEARY CARAVAN REACHES THE EUPHRATES RIVER AND THERE BELOW THEM, SURROUNDED BY LUXURIOUS GARDENS, IS THE MERCHANT'S HOUSE.

THE POMPOUS MASTER WADDLES ACROSS THE COURT-YARD, TWIRLING HIS MUSTACHE AND PUFFING OUT HIS CHEST.    SOMEHOW, THIS BRAVE, NEW SWORD MAKES HIM FEEL LIKE A BOLD AND RECKLESS FIGHTING MAN!

THE SLAVE QUARTERS ARE SEPARATED FROM THE HOUSE; THE GUARDS ARE MANY AND WATCHFUL, THE LABOR HARD.   VAL COMES NEARER TO DESPAIR THAN EVER BEFORE IN HIS LIFE...

THEN, ONE EVENING HE SEES A YOUNG MAIDEN CROSSING THE COURTYARD, BEAUTIFUL, LANGUID, PROUD.   "NOW, THERE," SAYS VAL BRUSHING BACK HIS HAIR AND GETTING UP.   "IS THE ANSWER TO MY PRAYER!"

NEXT WEEK— **The Answer.**

**Synopsis:** PRINCE VALIANT CANNOT BEGIN HIS QUEST FOR ALETA, QUEEN OF THE MISTY ISLES, UNTIL HE HAS REGAINED HIS CHARMED "SINGING SWORD". HE IS IMPATIENT; IMPATIENCE BREEDS A QUICK TEMPER AND A QUICK TEMPER BREEDS ENEMIES. HIS ENEMIES TRIUMPH AND BOTH VAL AND THE "SWORD" ARE SOLD TO BELSHAD ABU, A RICH SYRIAN MERCHANT.

A PRETTY MAID CROSSES THE COURT. "I WILL MAKE FRIENDS WITH HER," THINKS VAL, "THROUGH HER INFLUENCE I MAY BE ABLE TO ESCAPE."

BUT TO BERNICE, PAMPERED DAUGHTER OF BELSHAD ABU, A SLAVE IS ONLY A SLAVE AND PRINCELY MANNERS BUT ARROGANCE. SHE CALLS HER ATTENDANT.

A LAD OF SPIRIT DOES NOT LIKE TO BE ROUGHLY HANDLED BY AN ATTENDANT. THE SCREAMS OF BERNICE BRING A SWARM OF GUARDS AND THE TURBULENCE IS SOON QUELLED.

BERNICE TAKES VINDICTIVE PLEASURE IN WATCHING THE PUNISHMENT OF THE PRESUMPTUOUS SLAVE. SHE EVEN ORDERS A DOZEN EXTRA LASHES, BECAUSE HE DOES NOT CRY OUT WITH PAIN

PAIN AND DESPAIR ARE HIS COMPANIONS THIS NIGHT. HE, WHO HAD TROD THE PALACE OF KINGS, LED ARMIES AND SAT AT THE ROUND TABLE, IS A SLAVE, WHIPPED ON A PETULANT GIRL'S WHIM! IN HIS HEART IS MORE HATE THAN IS GOOD FOR A LAD OF SEVENTEEN.

NEXT MORNING A GREAT CHANGE HAS COME OVER VAL; HE HAS A SMILE, A BIT OF SONG.... AND A PLAN!

OFTEN, WHEN THE DAY'S BITTER TOIL IS DONE, SOME WEARY SLAVE WOULD POUR OUT HIS LONELINESS IN SOME SAD SONG OF HIS DISTANT HOMELAND.

THEN WOULD VAL SEIZE A LUTE AND THE DISMAL SLAVE-QUARTERS WOULD AWAKE TO A ROLLICKING BALLAD, A LOVE SONG OR A BATTLE-CHANT.

ON A DISTANT BALCONY BERNICE AWAKES FROM HER ROMANTIC DREAMING AND SITS UP. SO GAY AND VIBRANT A VOICE.... AND COMING FROM THE SLAVES' COMPOUND? SHE BECOMES INTERESTED.

NEXT WEEK— **The Karem Wall**

233  7-27-41

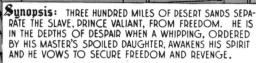

**Synopsis:** THREE HUNDRED MILES OF DESERT SANDS SEPARATE THE SLAVE, PRINCE VALIANT, FROM FREEDOM. HE IS IN THE DEPTHS OF DESPAIR WHEN A WHIPPING, ORDERED BY HIS MASTER'S SPOILED DAUGHTER, AWAKENS HIS SPIRIT AND HE VOWS TO SECURE FREEDOM AND REVENGE.

EACH NIGHT HE SOFTLY SINGS THE ROMANTIC LOVE-BALLADS OF ALL THE LANDS HE HAS VISITED. BERNICE HEARS; SHE LEAVES THE WOMEN'S QUARTERS AND COMES TO A LITTLE WINDOW ABOVE THE SLAVE-COMPOUND TO LISTEN. SHE IS INTERESTED, VAL HAS GAINED THE FIRST STEP.

IN THE FIELDS VAL SETS THE PACE; HE LAUGHS AND SINGS AND SHOUTS ENCOURAGEMENT. THE HOPELESS SLAVES RESPOND AND WORK LIKE MEN

AT EVENING, WHEN THE SLAVES DROP WEARILY TO REST, VAL WASHES AWAY THE STAINS OF TOIL AND BRUSHES HIS GLOSSY HAIR. HE MAKES HIMSELF IN ALL WAYS DIFFERENT FROM HIS FELLOWS.

AT LENGTH VAL IS REWARDED. HE HAS BECOME TOO GOOD A SLAVE FOR FIELD WORK AND IS MADE ONE OF THE HOUSEHOLD STAFF. ALTHOUGH HE KNOWS BUT A SMATTERING OF THE SYRIAN TONGUE, LATIN AND GREEK ARE UNIVERSAL LANGUAGES AND VAL KNOWS BOTH.

OFFICE WORK IS DULL OCCUPATION FOR A LAD OF SPIRIT, BUT VAL IS LEARNING PATIENCE, A VIRTUE HE DID NOT POSSESS BEFORE.

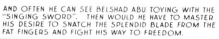

AND OFTEN HE CAN SEE BELSHAD ABU TOYING WITH THE "SINGING SWORD". THEN WOULD HE HAVE TO MASTER HIS DESIRE TO SNATCH THE SPLENDID BLADE FROM THE FAT FINGERS AND FIGHT HIS WAY TO FREEDOM.

WITH THE AID OF A STOLEN WINE-SKIN OR TWO VAL MAKES FRIENDS WITH THE LORDLY CAMEL-DRIVERS AND LEARNS THE CARAVAN ROUTES HE MUST EVENTUALLY USE.

ONE DAY HE FINDS THEM PREPARING FOR A JOURNEY; TOMORROW EVE BELSHAD ABU WILL DEPART TAKING THE SWORD WITH HIM. VAL MUST ACT AT ONCE!

234 8-3-41

"DEATH TO ANY MAN WHO VIOLATES THE SANCTITY OF THE WOMEN'S QUARTERS".....VAL LEAPS FOR THE TOP AND DRAWS HIMSELF OVER THE WALL!

NEXT WEEK — Elopement.

**Synopsis:** WHEN PRINCE VALIANT LEARNS THAT HIS MASTER, BELSHAD ABU, WILL LEAVE ON A JOURNEY THE NEXT EVENING, TAKING THE "SINGING SWORD" WITH HIM, HE ACTS AT ONCE. CLIMBING THE WALL HE DROPS INTO THE FORBIDDEN HAREM GARDENS.

ON HER BALCONY BERNICE IS ENJOYING THE COOL OF THE EVENING.

"CLIMBING TO A LADY'S BALCONY IS MORE IN SIR GAWAIN'S LINE," MUTTERS VAL. "MAY HEAVEN GRANT ME A GLIB TONGUE THIS NIGHT!"

"QUIET! OR I'LL WRING THAT PRETTY NECK!" ORDERS VAL. BERNICE'S EYES OPEN WIDE; NEVER, IN HER USELESS, LUXURIOUS LIFE, HAS ANYONE DARED TO SPEAK TO HER THUS. BUT SHE ALSO REMAINS QUIET.

"I AM PRINCE VALIANT, KNIGHT OF ARTHUR'S ROUND TABLE, HEIR TO THE KINGDOM OF THULE. WHEN, IN MY DISTANT HOMELAND, I HEARD TROUBADOURS TELL OF YOUR GREAT LOVELINESS, I TOOK SWORD AND SHIELD AND FOUGHT MY WAY ACROSS A THOUSAND LEAGUES OF HOSTILE LAND TO WIN TO YOUR SIDE!"

"AND I HAVE VOWED THAT I'LL NE'ER RETURN UNLESS YOU COME WITH ME. EVEN HAVE I SOLD MY SWORD AND MY BODY INTO SLAVERY, IN ORDER TO SEE AT LAST THE BEAUTY OF WHICH POETS SING. YOU ARE LIKE THE CRESCENT MOON, LOVELIER THAN THE SEA, YOUR MOUTH IS A FLOWER (HE KISSES IT). WE SHALL VISIT THE PALACES OF ALL THE KINGS UPON OUR WAY, THAT THEY MAY ENVY ME; FOR I SHALL TRAVEL AS A TRUE PRINCE. ......ORDER MY SWORD AND A SHIELD AND GOOD HORSES, WE WILL LEAVE AT ONCE! DON'T FORGET YOUR JEWELS, EITHER!"

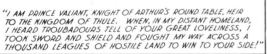

BERNICE IS SWEPT OFF HER FEET, BEWILDERED. ROMANCE HAS COME TO HER IN TOO BIG A PORTION. "I CAN'T, I AM AFRAID," SHE WAILS. "FATHER WOULDN'T LET ME." 8-10-41

VAL LEAPS TO HIS FEET. "MAY ALL THE GODS PITY ME," HE CRIES, "I HAVE GIVEN MY HEART TO BEAUTY, BUT SHE HAS NEITHER THE COURAGE NOR SPIRIT TO DARE!"

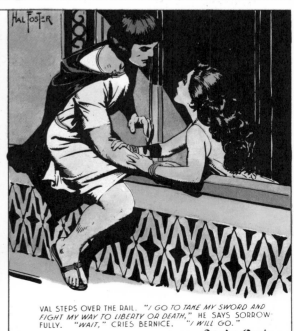

VAL STEPS OVER THE RAIL. "I GO TO TAKE MY SWORD AND FIGHT MY WAY TO LIBERTY OR DEATH," HE SAYS SORROWFULLY. "WAIT," CRIES BERNICE. "I WILL GO."

NEXT WEEK - **At the Oasis.**

**Synopsis:** WHEN THE TIME COMES PRINCE VALIANT ACTS. HE SCALES THE HAREM WALL, CLIMBS TO HER BALCONY AND MAKES SUCH IMPETUOUS LOVE TO BERNICE THAT SHE IS BEWILDERED. WHEN SHE FINDS OUT THIS HANDSOME YOUNG SLAVE IS INDEED A PRINCE SHE IS SWEPT OFF HER FEET.

"I'LL GO WITH YOU." SHE WHISPERS, TREMBLING WITH EXCITEMENT. "HORSES WILL BE WAITING AT THE STABLES IN AN HOUR." "...AND DON'T FORGET THE 'SINGING SWORD'...OR YOUR JEWELS," VAL ADDS.

THE GREAT SWORD IS TAKEN FROM ITS PLACE ON THE WALL

IN THE STABLE YARD VAL MEETS THEM. BERNICE HAS BROUGHT ALONG TWO ATTENDANTS, THEREBY INCREASING THE HAZARD OF DISCOVERY OR TREACHERY, BUT VAL DOESN'T MIND. HIS PLANS ARE COMPLETE.

ACROSS THE DESERT TOWARD DAMASCUS THEY GO, ARRIVING AT THE FIRST OASIS AFTER SUNUP.

ONE OF THE ATTENDANTS WEARS THE HELMET AND CHAIN-MAIL THAT VAL WILL NEED IN THE FUTURE, SO HE REMOVES THE OTHER ATTENDANT TEMPORARILY, SO HE WON'T INTERFERE.

"YOUR FACE IS VERY FAMILIAR," SAYS VAL, DRAWING HIS SWORD. "YOU ARE THE ONE WHO GAVE ME THE LASH, ARE YOU NOT?" THERE WAS, BY THAT TIME, NO POSSIBILITY OF AN ANSWER!

VAL TURNS TOWARD BERNICE AND THERE IS A LOOK ON HIS FACE THAT FRIGHTENS HER. SOMEHOW THIS ELOPEMENT IS NOT TURNING OUT AS SHE EXPECTED.

"THROUGH YOU, POOR, STUPID, SILKEN LITTLE FOOL, I HAVE REGAINED MY SWORD, MY LIBERTY AND MY FORTUNE. SO I SEND YOU BACK. AND WHY HAVE I USED YOU THUS? LET THE SCARS ON MY BACK, FROM THE WHIPPING YOU ORDERED, BE YOUR ANSWER!"

236 8-17-41

FREE! FREE AGAIN! WITH THE "SINGING SWORD" ONCE MORE AT HIS SIDE AND THE HIGH ROAD TO ADVENTURE BEFORE HIM. ......HE WATCHES THE SOBBING MAID RIDE AWAY...... AND SIGHS. (HE ALSO FEELS REMORSE.)

NEXT WEEK - **The Rage of Belshad Abu.**

Synopsis: PRINCE VALIANT ESCAPES FROM SLAVERY BY THE SIMPLE METHOD OF MAKING LOVE TO BERNICE, THE MASTER'S DAUGHTER. FOR THEIR ELOPEMENT THE PAMPERED LITTLE DARLING SUPPLIES VAL WITH EVERYTHING, INCLUDING THE "SINGING SWORD". AT THE FIRST OASIS HE SENDS HER BACK HOME.

VAL SITS BY THE DESERT WELL, FEELING PRETTY MEAN..... SHE HAD SEEMED FOND OF HIM.

BERNICE IS BROKEN-HEARTED! WHY DID THIS TALL YOUTH HAVE TO TAKE A WHIPPING SO SERIOUSLY? PERHAPS SHE SHOULDN'T HAVE ORDERED THOSE TWELVE EXTRA LASHES. HE WAS SO FIERCE, SO HANDSOME AND ALSO A BIT FRIGHTENING. FOR THE FIRST TIME IN HER LIFE SHE COULDN'T HAVE WHAT SHE WANTED!

ABOUT THIS TIME BELSHAD ABU DISCOVERS THE "SINGING SWORD" IS MISSING AND A SCREAM OF ANGUISH FILLS THE HOUSE.

HE IS INCONSOLABLE, HIS TREASURE! HIS NOBLE BLADE! HE IS TOLD THAT HIS DAUGHTER IS ALSO MISSING AND HE IS SORRY ABOUT THAT, TOO..... BUT THE SCABBARD WAS JEWELED AND IT WAS SO EXPENSIVE!.....

HE ORDERS HIS DANCING GIRLS TO SYMPATHIZE WITH HIM...TELLS THEM HOW THE MAGIC PROPERTIES OF THE SWORD MADE HIM FEEL SO BRAVE THAT SOME DAY HE MIGHT HAVE DONE A NOBLE DEED..."AND NOT FOR PROFIT, EITHER," HE EXPLAINS.

TOWARD LATE AFTERNOON THE FORLORN BERNICE RETURNS. BELSHAD ABU FOLDS HER IN HIS ARMS. "WHERE'S MY SWORD?" HE ASKS. "ON THE ROAD TO DAMASCUS WITH MY HEART," SHE SOBS.

THEN THE ARMED HORSEMEN OF BELSHAD ABU RUSH FROM THE GATE, EAGER TO EARN THE EXTRAVAGANT REWARD OFFERED FOR SWORD AND SLAVE.

BUT PRINCE VALIANT HAS FOLLOWED BERNICE BACK ALMOST TO THE GATE AND, FROM A DISTANCE, SEES THE HORSEMEN FLASH BY ON A WILD-GOOSE CHASE.

237 8-24-41

THEN HE TURNS WESTWARD, UP THE EUPHRATES ON THE CARAVAN ROUTE TO ALEPPO.

NEXT WEEK— The Djinn.

**Synopsis:** PRINCE VALIANT SPEEDS WESTWARD ALONG THE EUPHRATES. AT TIMES HE RIDES RECKLESSLY, NOT THAT HE FEARS RE-CAPTURE; AS HE HAS ALREADY SENT HIS PURSUERS ON A WILD-GOOSE-CHASE; BUT IN SHEER ENJOYMENT OF HIS FREEDOM. FOR NO ONE WHO HAS NOT SUFFERED SLAVERY CAN FULLY APPRECIATE FREEDOM.

FREE! FREE AGAIN! AND WITH THE "SINGING SWORD" ONCE MORE AT HIS SIDE, VAL CAN AGAIN GO QUEST-ING FOR ALETA, QUEEN OF THE MISTY ISLES.

WHERE THE RIVER CUTS THROUGH THE MOUNTAINS, VAL BEHOLDS A STRANGE SIGHT. A STRING OF DONKEYS ISSUES FROM A NARROW CLEFT AND ON EACH SIDE TRAVELERS HAVE DRAWN BACK IN TERROR!

RIDING UP, VAL ASKS THE REASON. *"BEYOND YONDER DARK CLEFT LIVES AN EVIL DJINN,"* REPLIES A TRAVELER. *"EACH DAY HE SENDS DEAD MEN TO THE RIVER TO FETCH WATER!"*

BY THIS TIME THE DONKEYS ARE RETURNING FROM THE RIVER, THEIR WATER-SKINS FILLED. VAL IS HORRIFIED AT THE APPEARANCE OF THE DRIVERS.

WISE MERLIN, COURT MAGICIAN TO KING ARTHUR ONCE TOLD VAL; *"A MYSTERY, WHEN SOLVED IS MERE FACTS, MAGIC, WHEN EXPLAINED, IS BUT SCIENCE."* DESPITE ALL WARNINGS, VAL TURNS UP THE CLEFT.

A FEW MILES FARTHER AND THE MAGI'S GRAY TOWER COMES INTO VIEW, SILENT AND FORBIDDING. *"AN EVIL BIRD HAS EVER AN EVIL NEST,"* QUOTES VAL, SHUDDERING.

WHILE CIRCLING THE SILENT WALLS, VAL HEARS AN OMINOUS COUGH AND, LOOK-ING UP, SEES A WITCH-WOMAN AT A HIGH WINDOW. WITHOUT EVEN GLANCING AT HIM SHE RINGS A DINNER-BELL. IT MAKES VAL FEEL VAGUELY UNCOMFORTABLE.

AT THE "ENTRANCE" HE STOPS. THE THRESHOLD IS FRESHLY SCRUBBED AND A MAT WITH "WELCOME" ON IT IN NEAT LETTERS IS PLACED OUTSIDE AND "WELCOME" ALSO IS PAINTED ON THE DOOR IN SEVERAL LANGUAGES. BUT THE EXIT HAS AN UN-WHOLESOME LOOK AND DEPARTING GUESTS SEEM TO HAVE LEFT SOUVENIRS THEY MUST HAVE VALUED AT ONE TIME OR ANOTHER. NEXT WEEK- *Val meets the Magi.*

238 8-31-41

HAL FOSTER

# Prince Valiant

IN THE DAYS OF
KING ARTHUR
BY
HAROLD R FOSTER

BELSATAN

**Synopsis:** PRINCE VALIANT LOOKS FIRST AT THE »ENTRANCE« THEN AT THE OMINOUS »EXIT« AND SHUDDERS. »OH! WELL, CURIOSITYV HAS BROUGHT ME THIS FAR«. HE SAYS WITH A SHRUG. »MIGHT AS WELL SEE IT THROUGH.« AND HE RAISES HIS FIST TO KNOCK...

.....BUT BEFORE HE CAN KNOCK THE GATES SWING WIDE AND TWO OF THOSE GHASTLY RETAINERS STAND ASIDE.

MASKING HIS DREAD WITH A CARELESS SMILE, VAL ENTERS, HIS HAND RESTING ON HIS SWORD. THEY STABLE HIS TWO HORSES, THEN LEAD THE WAY.....

.....THROUGH MANY A PONDEROUS DOOR, STONE PASSAGEWAY AND WINDING STAIRWAY THEY LEAD HIM.

FAR IN THE DIM INTERIOR THEY HALT BEFORE A FLIMSY DOOR, FROM WITHIN COMES THE SHRILL TUMULT OF A VIOLENT QUARREL, VAL KNOCKS, «COME IN!» ROARS A DEEP VOICE

"OH! GOODNESS!.....COME IN, COME IN.... MOST EMBARRASSING; FAMILY DISCUSSION...... MUST PARDON US ...AND ALL THAT...."

"VISITORS ALWAYS WELCOME, MEET ACIDIA, MY WIFE, A FAMOUS BEAUTY IN HER DAY.....WIFE! SET ANOTHER PLATE FOR SUPPER, WE'LL HAVE A GUEST!"

SO PRINCE VALIANT DINES WITH THE MAGUS BELSATAN AND HIS PRETTY WIFE, ACIDIA.
"MY SERVANTS?" SAYS BELSATAN IN ANSWER TO A QUESTION FROM VAL, "THEY HAVE ALWAYS BEEN HERE. SOME OF MY GRANDFATHER'S WORK, I THINK . THEY'RE VERY HANDY, PRACTICALLY NO UPKEEP AT ALL!"

"THEY LEAVE ME FREE TO ATTEND TO MY WORK VERY IMPORTANT. WORK, TOO; FOR I AM NOW WEAVING DREAMS....DREAMS THROUGH WHICH PEOPLE CAN MEET AND CONVERSE IN THE HALF-WORLD, NO MATTER HOW FAR APART THEIR BODIES MAY BE...."

239 9-7-41

"CAN YOU CONTRIVE A DREAM FOR ME?" CRIES VAL, HIS EYES SHINING WITH EXCITEMENT. "A DREAM THROUGH WHICH I CAN KNOW FOR SURE IF ALETA IS REAL OR BUT A VISION?"
"I CAN TRY." SAYS BELSATAN, "IT WILL MAKE AN INTERESTING EXPERIMENT."
NEXT WEEK— **The Dream.**

HAL FOSTER

**Synopsis:** BECAUSE THE SPIRIT OF ADVENTURE IS STRONG WITHIN HIS HEART, PRINCE VALIANT ENTERS THE DREAD TOWER OF BELSATAN, THE MAGUS. THIS SKILLED "MASTER OF DARKNESS" HAS FOR A HOBBY THE WEAVING OF DREAMS AND VAL IMMEDIATELY ASKS IF HE CAN OBTAIN NEWS OF ALETA THROUGH BELSATAN'S ART.

"AN INTERESTING EXPERIMENT!" EXCLAIMS BELSATAN ENTHUSIASTICALLY. "IN YOUR SLEEP YOU CAN MEET THIS FAIR ALETA, QUEEN OF THE MISTY ISLES, AND FIND WHETHER SHE BE REAL OR BUT A FANCY."

IN HIS WORKSHOP, AT MIDNIGHT, BELSATAN PERFORMS STRANGE RITES AND INCANTATIONS......AND THE THING IS DONE!

VAL HURRIES TO HIS ROOM. HE IS GREATLY EXCITED, FOR AT LAST HE WILL LEARN THE TRUTH!

FOR A LONG TIME HE LISTENS TO THE QUARRELING FROM THE NEXT ROOM; BELSATAN, THOUGH THE GREATEST MAGUS OF THE EAST, HAS YET FOUND NO WAY OF CONTROLLING HIS WIFE'S TONGUE!

THEN THE BRIGHT SYRIAN MOON LIGHTS UP THE ROOM AND A SWARM OF MOSQUITOES COMES IN THROUGH THE OPEN WINDOW.

VAL DRAWS THE BED-CURTAINS AND BURROWS BENEATH THE COVERS, BUT IT BECOMES TOO HOT AND STUFFY FOR SLEEP....HE TOSSES AND TURNS RESTLESSLY FOR HOURS.

IN THE COOL OF THE DAWN, WHEN DREAMS HAVE FLOWN, HE SINKS AT LAST INTO SLEEP.

BELSATAN HAS ALSO GONE SLEEPLESS. HE HAD MARRIED ACIDIA FOR HER BEAUTY, HER CRITICAL DISPOSITION AND SHARP TONGUE ARE THINGS HE HADN'T FIGURED ON.

240 9-14-41

AT BREAKFAST ACIDIA WEARS THE SATISFIED EXPRESSION OF A WIFE WHO HAS TOLD HER HUSBAND A LOT OF THINGS FOR HIS OWN GOOD; VAL IS PALE AND DISAPPOINTED, BUT BELSATAN IS IN GREAT GOOD HUMOR....FOR HE HAS CONCOCTED A SCHEME WHEREBY HE WILL RID HIMSELF OF A NUISANCE!

NEXT WEEK— *The Enforced Elopement.*

HAL FOSTER

BELSATAN

**Synopsis:** PRINCE VALIANT SITS AT BREAKFAST WITH BELSATAN, THE MAGICIAN, AND ACIDIA, HIS BEAUTIFUL BUT SHARP-TONGUED WIFE. BELSATAN IS IN HIGH GOOD-HUMOR FOR HE HAS DEVISED A SCHEME TO RID HIM-SELF OF HIS NAGGING SPOUSE.

"WHAT A BEAUTIFUL DAY FOR A PICNIC," COOS BELSATAN. "ACIDIA, DARLING, WHY DON'T YOU TAKE OUR GUEST TO SEE THE CRYSTAL CAVERNS? IT IS A NICE RIDE AND YOU LOOK SO CHARMING ON HORSEBACK....OF COURSE," HE ADDS, "NO ONE DARES ENTER THE CAVERNS."

THE WILY OLD ROGUE GUESSED RIGHT; THE HINT OF DANGER IS ENOUGH TO SEND VAL TO THE CAVERNS AND THAT REMARK ABOUT LOOKING LOVELY ON A HORSE TOUCHES ACIDIA'S VANITY.

SO THEY TAKE A LUNCH, AND CHATTING GAILY, RIDE AWAY.

THEN BELSATAN ASCENDS TO THE TOWER ROOF AND CONJURES UP A GREAT STORM......

.....WHICH, BURSTING WITH SUDDEN VIOLENCE, WELL-NIGH DROWNS THE SPUTTERING MAGUS BEFORE HE CAN GAIN SHELTER!

WHEN VAL RETURNS FROM EXPLORING THE CAVERN, THE STORM IS RAGING WILDLY AND TRAVEL IS IMPOSSIBLE.

ALL NIGHT LONG THEY SIT OVER A SMALL FIRE, WAITING FOR THE TEMPEST TO ABATE.

BUT NEXT DAY, WHEN THEY RETURN, THE TOWER IS LOCKED AND BARRED AGAINST THEM. "OUT OF MY SIGHT, FAITHLESS WOMAN!" ROARS BELSATAN, "BEGONE, FALSE FRIEND WHO WOULD KEEP MY WIFE OUT ALL NIGHT.... AWAY, SHAMELESS ONES!"

241 9-21-41

HASTILY HE CLOSES THE WINDOW ON HIS WIFE'S SHRILL REMARKS AND DANCES A HAPPY JIG. "FREE AGAIN AT LAST.... NOW FOR A HAPPY BACHELOR'S LIFE. NO ONE TO MEDDLE IN MY WORK, NO NAGGING! WHAT A CLEVER FELLOW IS BELSATAN, THE MAGUS!"

NEXT WEEK — *The Bachelor's Life.*

**Synopsis:** BELSATAN, THE WIZARD, GETS RID OF ACIDIA, HIS PRETTY SHARP-TONGUED, NAGGING WIFE BY SENDING HER ON A PICNIC WITH PRINCE VALIANT AND THEN CREATING A STORM THAT KEEPS THEM OUT ALL NIGHT. IN A VIOLENT, BUT PHONY RAGE, HE SENDS THE FAITHLESS ONES AWAY.

VAL SUSPECTS HE HAS BEEN TRICKED, BUT THE RULES OF CHIVALRY DEMAND HE PROTECT THIS HOMELESS LADY.

CHUCKLING HAPPILY, BELSATAN SEATS HIMSELF AT HIS WORK-TABLE. 'NOW FOR A GOOD DAY'S WORK UNATTENDED BY STRIFE AND TURMOIL!'

BUT THE UNACCUSTOMED SILENCE MAKES HIM NERVOUS.....EVERYTHING IS SO STILL! HE FINDS HIMSELF LISTENING INSTEAD OF CONCENTRATING!

AFTER A VERY UNSATISFACTORY DAY HE GOES IN TO SUPPER, BUT IS GREETED ONLY WITH THE SOILED BREAKFAST DISHES....NO ONE HAS ORDERED SUPPER!

HE FINDS A FEW COLD LEFT-OVERS IN THE PANTRY AND WANDERS OFF TO BED; THE LIGHTS ARE NOT LIT; THE FURNITURE JUST WHERE HE LEFT IT AND THE BED UNMADE

ON TOP OF ALL THIS HE HAS MISLAID HIS NIGHT-CAP AND AWAKES WITH THE SNIFFLES. HE ALSO IS QUITE CERTAIN THAT HE WILL HAVE TO GET HIS OWN BREAKFAST

MEANWHILE VAL LISTENS TO A STEADY FLOW OF CONVERSATION; "OH! TO THINK I'VE GIVEN THE BEST CENTURIES OF MY LIFE TO THAT UNGRATEFUL WRETCH. I'VE HAD TO WATCH HIM LIKE A BABY OR HE'D CATCH COLD OR GET SICK FROM OVEREATING......

242 9-28-41

"....EVEN NOW I'LL BET HE'S CONJURED UP SOME SILLY GIRLS TO KEEP HIM COMPANY, THE OLD FOOL! I CAN JUST IMAGINE THE MESS HE'LL MAKE....MY LINEN....MY SILVERWARE! OH! IF I COULD ONLY GIVE THE MISERABLE INSECT A PIECE OF MY MIND!"

HAL FOSTER

BELSATAN, THE GREATEST WIZARD IN ALL ASIA, HAS JUST MADE A TERRIFIC DISCOVERY; THAT A WIFE IS IMPOSSIBLE TO LIVE WITH BUT WORSE TO BE WITHOUT!

NEXT WEEK- *Belsatan's Great Magic.*

# Prince Valiant

BELSATAN

**Synopsis.....** AS PRINCE VALIANT ESCORTS THE LADY ACIDIA WESTWARD, HE MARVELS AT THE OVERPOWERING VOLUME OF HER CHATTER. FOR SHE IS AN ABANDONED WIFE, RE-COUNTING HER HUSBAND'S SHORTCOMINGS....AND THEY ARE ENDLESS!

MEANWHILE, BELSATAN, THE GREAT WIZARD, HAS MADE THE DISCOVERY THAT LONELINESS WILL NOT YIELD TO MAGIC. HE COULD NOT LIVE COMFORTABLY WITH HIS WIFE, BUT ANYTHING IS BETTER THAN THE UNACCUSTOMED PEACE AND QUIET WHICH IS DRIV-ING HIM FRANTIC!

SO HE DRAWS THE "MAGIC CIRCLE" AND THE SIX-POINTED STAR OF HA-MLOO, SETS OUT THE APPROPRIATE SYMBOLS, DOES WHAT IS NECESSARY BY WAY OF SACRIFICE (WE NEED NOT RECOUNT THE HORRORS OF THIS PROCEDURE) AND, WITH FEAR IN HIS HEART, RECITES THE LONG, WEIRD INCANTATION.

WHAT HAPPENED WAS BEYOND DESCRIPTION! THE TOWER ROCKED TO ITS FOUNDATIONS AND EARTHQUAKES WERE FELT THROUGHOUT ALL ASIA. BELSATAN MADE HIS REQUEST AND PAID A CERTAIN TERRIBLE PRICE.......

HAL FOSTER

VAL IS STARTLED BY A SUDDEN FLASH AND ROAR.....THEN A CALM AND PEACEFUL SILENCE......ACIDIA IS GONE!

"HELLO, WIFE DEAR." SAYS BELSATAN MEEKLY FROM AMID THE WRECKAGE......THEN HE SETTLES BACK COMFORTABLY, WHILE ABOUT HIS EARS HUMS THE ACCUSTOMED CLATTER OF AN ABUSED WIFE, RECOUNTING THE FAULTS AND FAILINGS OF AN IMPOSSIBLE HUSBAND. ONCE MORE THE TOWER HAS A HOMEY FEELING!

NEXT WEEK— **A Wandering Knight from Home**

243 10-5-41

**Synopsis:** AFTER MANY STRANGE ADVENTURES PRINCE VALIANT IS FREE ONCE MORE TO CONTINUE HIS DIFFICULT SEARCH FOR ALETA, QUEEN OF THE MISTY ISLES.

LEAVING THE EUPHRATES RIVER, HE CROSSES THE STONY DESERT TO ALEPPO.

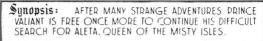

WESTWARD LIE ANTIOCH AND THE SEA....AND BEFORE HIM AN ARMORED KNIGHT FIGHTS FURIOUSLY AGAINST A GROUP OF SARACENS!

VAL HAS GOOD REASON TO HATE THE DESERT-MEN, SO, DRAWING FORTH THE "SINGING SWORD" HE CHARGES TO THE ASSISTANCE OF THE STRANGE KNIGHT.

"NOW WHY IN HEAVEN'S NAME SHOULD A DARK INFIDEL HELD A CHRISTIAN KNIGHT?"
"I AM NOT AN INFIDEL, BUT A CHRISTIAN," SAYS VAL, "REMOVE THAT IRON POT IN WHICH YOUR WITS ARE STEWING, AND LET ME SEE WHO TALKS ENGLISH IN THIS BARBAROUS LAND."

"SIR ASTOMORE, KNIGHT OF KING ARTHUR'S ROUND TABLE!" EXCLAIMS VAL, THROWING HIS ARMS AROUND THE AGED KNIGHT'S NECK. "WHY ARE YOU ROAMING THIS CRUEL LAND?"

"AGE HAS RENDERED ME UNFIT TO FURTHER SERVE MY KING, SO I AM JOURNEYING TO JERUSALEM TO DIE IN THE HOLY CITY." AND HE TELLS OF HIS LONELY BLUNDERINGS ACROSS STRANGE LANDS.

THE SIMPLE FAITH OF THIS GALLANT OLD WARRIOR AWAKES IN VAL MEMORIES OF WINDY THULE: HIS FATHER'S KINGDOM: OF ENGLAND AND THE BOISTEROUS COURT OF KING ARTHUR... A WAVE OF HOMESICKNESS GRIPS HIM......

.....SO HE TURNS FROM HIS WAY TO GUIDE SIR ASTOMORE TO JERUSALEM. SOUTHWARD THEY RIDE THROUGH «THE HOLLOW LAND OF SYRIA». THE FERTILE VALLEY THAT HAS BEEN THE ROADWAY FOR INVADING ARMIES SINCE TIME BEGAN.....AND IS AGAIN TODAY.

244  10-12-41.

BEFORE THE CHURCH OF THE HOLY SEPULCHRE VAL STOPS AND THE AGED KNIGHT GOES ON ALONE TO THE END OF HIS QUEST, HIS SILVERY HAIR SHINING IN THE SUN.

NEXT WEEK — **Unfinished Business.**

HAL FOSTER

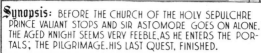

**Synopsis:** BEFORE THE CHURCH OF THE HOLY SEPULCHRE PRINCE VALIANT STOPS AND SIR ASTOMORE GOES ON ALONE. THE AGED KNIGHT SEEMS VERY FEEBLE, AS HE ENTERS THE PORTALS; THE PILGRIMAGE. HIS LAST QUEST, FINISHED.

VAL WATCHES THE OLD WARRIOR DISAPPEAR, THEN TURNS BACK. FOR ANGOR WRACK HAS A HOUSE IN JERUSALEM AND HE AND VAL HAVE SOME UNFINISHED BUSINESS TOGETHER.

"THIS TIME WE WILL SETTLE THE DISPUTED OWNERSHIP OF THE 'SINGING SWORD' TO EVERYONE'S SATISFACTION."

SOMBELENE AND ANGOR WRACK SEE HIM COMING: "FRANKLY, I LIKE THAT HOT-HEADED YOUNG IDIOT. HE IS RISKING HIS LIFE OVER THE OWNERSHIP OF A SWORD ALREADY HIS."

LOOSENING HIS BLADE IN THE SCABBARD, THE "YOUNG IDIOT" RAPS UPON THE DOOR.

IN THE DARK HALLWAY HE IS SEIZED SUDDENLY AND THE "SINGING SWORD" TORN FROM HIS GRASP!

"SIR VALIANT. AS LONG AS YOU THINK I HAVE SOME CLAIM ON THE 'SINGING SWORD', YOU WILL BE FOREVER FIGHTING ME FOR IT AND I CAN'T SPEND ALL MY LIFE FIGHTING WITH YOU. MY WIFE DOESN'T LIKE IT."

...."SO I HAVE TAKEN IT. IT IS MINE TO DO WITH AS I PLEASE. SO I GIVE IT TO YOU."

245 10-19-41

VAL WALKS TO A TABLE AND SOLEMNLY POURS TWO GOBLETS OF WINE. "HERE, DRINK TO MY GREAT LOSS, FOR I HAVE LOST A SPLENDID ENEMY." THEY DRINK IN SILENCE.

HAL FOSTER

AGAIN VAL FILLS THE GOBLETS. "AND NOW," HE CRIES "DRINK TO MY GOOD FORTUNE, FOR I HAVE FOUND A FRIEND!"

NEXT WEEK— **Val's Birthday.**

**Synopsis:** PRINCE VALIANT AND ANGOR WRACK AT LAST SETTLE THEIR BITTER QUARREL AND BECOME FAST FRIENDS. VAL IS CONTENT TO BE HIS GUEST AND REST FROM HIS ADVENTURES.

ANGOR WRACK, SOMBELENE AND VAL SPEND MANY HAPPY HOURS TOGETHER.

BUT TURBULENCE AND ADVENTURE ARE IN HIS BLOOD. THE VISION OF ALETA'S LOVELY FACE HAUNTS HIS DREAMS AND HE HAS A LONGING FOR THE COOL OF HIS NORTHERN HOMELAND.

"IT WAS THROUGH YOU THAT SOMBELENE BECAME MY BRIDE", SAYS ANGOR WRACK, "IN GRATITUDE I WILL AID YOU IN YOUR SEARCH."

SO THEY CLOSE THE JERUSALEM HOUSE AND JOURNEY TO JAFFA, WHERE ANGOR WRACK FITS OUT A SHIP TO SEARCH THE AEGEAN SEAS.

AND ON THE AFTER-DECK OF THE LITTLE SHIP THE THREE FRIENDS CELEBRATE PRINCE VALIANT'S EIGHTEENTH BIRTHDAY.

FROM THE DECK OF HIS GREAT SHIP-OF-WAR ANGOR WRACK AND HIS BRIDE WATCH VAL SAIL AWAY — THEN THEY, TOO, SET SAIL TO PILLAGE THE DISTANT SEAS; FOR ANGOR WRACK IS STILL THE SEA-KING.

SO VAL GOES QUESTING ACROSS WIDE SEAS, BECAUSE OF A LOVELY FACE HE SAW BUT ONCE IN A VISION.

HAL FOSTER

AND THE SHIP'S CAPTAIN LOOKS WITH GREEDY EYES UPON THE JEWELS IN THE HILT OF THE "SINGING SWORD" AND WONDERS HOW MUCH MONEY THEY WILL BRING HIM.

NEXT WEEK — **A Fish Dinner.**

246  10-26-41

# Prince Valiant

IN THE DAYS OF
KING ARTHUR
BY
HAROLD R FOSTER

ALETA
QUEEN OF THE MISTY ISLES

Synopsis: IN SEARCH OF ALETA, QUEEN OF THE MISTY ISLES, PRINCE VALIANT SAILS FOR THE AEGEAN SEA IN A SHIP FITTED OUT BY HIS ERSTWHILE ENEMY, ANGOR WRACK.

ON A FOGGY MORNING A CORSAIR SUDDENLY APPEARS CLOSE ALONGSIDE AND PANIC SWEEPS THE CREW.

THE COWARDLY CAPTAIN ORDERS THE SHIP ABOUT AND SCREAMS TO HIS CREW TO OUT OARS AND ROW FOR THEIR LIVES.

RUN FROM AN ENEMY? SUCH A PROCEDURE MAKES VAL BLUSH FOR SHAME. AT THE PRICE OF A SKINNED KNUCKLE, HE TAKES COMMAND OF THE SHIP.

"TAKE YOUR WEAPONS!" HE ROARS. "AND THEN WE'LL TAKE THE PIRATE SHIP!"

NEVER WAS A PIRATE CREW SO OUTRAGED; FOR, AS THEY GRIND ALONGSIDE THEIR VICTIM, AN ARMED KNIGHT COMES LEAPING JOYOUSLY OVER THEIR RAIL AND SLASHES TREMENDOUSLY AMONGST THEM WITH A BLADE THAT SHRIEKS LIKE A LIVING THING!

THE SAILORS FOLLOW, SHOWING AS MUCH MERCY TO THE CONFUSED PIRATES, AS WAS THE CUSTOM IN THOSE DAYS. THEN THEY LOOT THE CAPTURED SHIP OF ITS RICH CARGO.

"WHAT A GREAT LEADER THE YOUNG KNIGHT WILL MAKE. WE WILL BECOME PIRATES AND WAX WEALTHY UNDER HIS COMMAND."

SO THE CREW DECIDES ON A LIFE OF PIRACY UNDER VAL. IN ORDER TO MAKE THINGS EASIER, THEY FALL UPON THEIR COWARDLY CAPTAIN IN THE DARK AND MAKE HIM RESIGN HIS COMMAND.

247 11-2-41

NEXT WEEK— But they don't become Pirates.

**Synopsis:** PRINCE VALIANT GOES QUESTING FAR AND WIDE AMONG THE AEGEAN ISLANDS, SEARCHING FOR ALETA AND THE MISTY ISLES. A CORSAIR ATTACKS THEM, BUT, UNDER VAL'S LEADERSHIP, THEY SURPRISE THE PIRATES AND CAPTURE A RICH CARGO.

AFTER MURDERING THEIR COWARDLY CAPTAIN, THE GREEDY CREW PLANS TO OFFER THE COMMAND TO VAL AND BECOME PIRATES, THEMSELVES, HOPING THE YOUNG KNIGHT WILL DO MOST OF THE FIGHTING.

THEIR SPOKESMAN EXPLAINS THAT THE CAPTAIN FELL OVER-BOARD AND VAL ACCEPTS THEIR REQUEST TO TAKE OVER.

THE CREW IS GREATLY DISAPPOINTED WHEN THEIR YOUNG LEADER REFUSES TO ROB PASSING MERCHANT SHIPS.....THEY NEVER EXPECTED SUCH HONESTY!

"YOU MEN WANTED A FIGHT, NOW YOU'LL HAVE IT!! A STRANGE SHIP IS PURSUING US, SO FOLLOW MY ORDERS CLOSELY AND WE'LL RID THE SEAS OF ANOTHER PIRATE!"

BUNDLES OF CLOTH ARE BOUND TO THE OARS AND SOAKED WITH OIL. AS THE CORSAIR RASPS ALONG-SIDE, THESE ARE IGNITED AND THRUST AMONG THE PIRATES.

FOLLOWING THIS WALL OF FLAME, COME VAL AND HIS ARMED FOLLOWERS. ALTHOUGH GREATLY OUTNUMBERED, A VICTORY IS WON......

.....BUT NOT WITHOUT COST. ALTHOUGH MORE RICH PLUNDER IS STORED AWAY, THE CREW IS FRIGHT-ENED.... THEY WISH ONLY TO POUNCE ON UNARMED MERCHANTMEN, NOT TACKLE FIERCE PIRATES!

THEIR NEW LEADER IS A HORNET FAR TOO DANGEROUS FOR THEIR LIKING. SO, WHEN NEXT HE LANDS IN HIS SEARCH FOR THE MISTY ISLES, THEY SAIL AWAY WITHOUT HIM.

Copr. 1941. King Features Syndicate, Inc. World rights reserved       248  11-9-41

RETURNING TO THE BEACH, VAL FINDS A STORM RAGING, BUT NO SIGN OF THE SHIP.
NEXT WEEK— **The Misty Isles.**

HAL FOSTER

# Prince Valiant

IN THE DAYS OF
KING ARTHUR
BY
HAROLD R FOSTER

ALETA
QUEEN OF THE MISTY ISLES

**Synopsis:** WHEN THE SHIP'S CREW MADE PRINCE VALIANT THEIR LEADER, THEY THOUGHT TO BECOME PIRATES. INSTEAD, HE LEADS THEM ONLY AGAINST FIERCE CORSAIRS AND THEY BECAME FRIGHTENED. AT THE FIRST OPPORTUNITY THEY MAROON HIM ON AN ISLAND.

VAL THINKS THE STORM HAS DRIVEN THEM OFF SHORE AND SETTLES HIMSELF IN A CAVE TO AWAIT THE SHIP'S RETURN.

THE RASCALLY SAILORS HAVE NO INTENTION OF RETURNING. LOADED WITH PLUNDER TAKEN FROM THE TWO DEFEATED CORSAIRS, THEIR SHIP WALLOWS AWAY THROUGH THE STORM.

ALL NIGHT AND ALL NEXT DAY THEY DRIVE BEFORE THE WIND. JUST AS DARKNESS FALLS, THEY APPROACH A STRANGE ISLAND AND FIND A SHELTERED HARBOR.

HERE THEY FURL THE SAILS AND DROP ANCHOR. THE LIGHTS OF A VILLAGE ARE GLEAMING THROUGH THE DARKNESS.

THEY GO ASHORE AND FIND THE SETTLEMENT UNGUARDED. THE MEN, CAUGHT OFF SHORE BY THE STORM, HAD SAILED THEIR FISHING-BOATS TO A DISTANT HAVEN.

THEN BEGINS A NIGHT OF TERROR. THEY ROB AND ABUSE THE HELPLESS WOMEN AND CHILDREN. THEY LOOT AND BURN THE VILLAGE......

.....AND AT DAWN THEY RETURN TO THEIR SHIP, LEAVING BEHIND DEED THAT CRIES ALOUD FOR VENGEANCE. THEY DO NOT KNOW THAT THIS ISLAND IS RULED BY A YOUNG QUEEN NAMED 'ALETA

THEY SAIL AWAY BLINDLY, SEEKING ONLY TO ESCAPE THE PUNISHMENT THEY HAD EARNED. THEN FATE TAKES A HAND AND THEY TAKE SHELTER IN THE VERY COVE FROM WHICH THEY HAD STARTED!

Copr. 1941, King Features Syndicate, Inc., World rights reserved      249  11-16-41

"FORGIVE US, NOBLE SIR, WE WERE DRIVEN FAR AWAY BY THE STORM AND HAVE SUFFERED GREAT HARDSHIP IN RETURNING FOR YOU." SO THEY LIE.

HAL FOSTER

NEXT WEEK— The Misty Isles.

**Synopsis:** THE CREW LEAVES PRINCE VALIANT MAROONED ON AN ISLAND AND SNEAKS OFF, BUT THE WIND CHANGES AND BLOWS THEM BACK AGAIN. THE RASCALS TELL VAL THE STORM HAD DRIVEN THEM AWAY. THEY DO NOT TELL HIM THAT, MEANWHILE, THEY HAD PLUNDERED AND BURNED A HELPLESS VILLAGE, WHILE ITS MENFOLK WERE AWAY.

WITH REEFED SAIL THEY SET OUT ONCE MORE ON THE SEARCH FOR THE MISTY ISLES.

VAL BELIEVES THE SAILORS ARE FAITHFUL, HONEST MEN, BUT EVEN NOW THEY ARE PLOTTING TO GET RID OF A LEADER WHO SEEMS TO LOVE DANGER FAR TOO MUCH FOR THEIR TASTES.

A SUDDEN SQUALL DRIVES DOWN UPON THEM AND, BEFORE THE SAILS CAN BE TRIMMED TO MEET IT, CARRIES AWAY MASTS AND SPARS.

"IF I CAN FASTEN A ROPE TO YONDER ROCK, THE SHIP WILL SWING INTO THE SHELTER OF THE HARBOR BEHIND." VAL TAKES ONE END OF THE ROPE AND LEAPS INTO THE ANGRY SEA.

EXHAUSTED, BRUISED AND BLEEDING, VAL IS JUST ABLE TO FASTEN THE ROPE AND THE SHIP SWINGS AROUND INTO THE LEE.

THEN, AND NOT TILL THEN, THE SAILORS DISCOVER THAT FATE HAS RETURNED THEM TO THE SCENE OF THEIR HORRIBLE CRIME!

THE SLENDER ROPE PARTS AND VAL IS LEFT, EXHAUSTED, ON THE WIND-SWEPT ROCK. AS THE SHIP DRIFTS SLOWLY SHOREWARD, ARMED MEN APPEAR FROM A RUINED VILLAGE. ANGRY SHOUTS RING OUT. THE SAILORS SCREAM.......

.... AND THEN, BEFORE HIS VERY EYES, HIS BRAVE CREW, HIS FAITHFUL COMPANIONS, ARE KILLED IN A HORRIBLE MANNER!

250  11-23-41  Copr. 1941, King Features Syndicate, Inc., World rights reserved

THE YOUNG PRINCE DOES NOT KNOW HOW RICHLY HIS MEN HAD EARNED THEIR PUNISHMENT. HE ONLY KNOWS THAT THIS ISLAND AND ALL IT CONTAINS IS EVIL, CRUEL, BAD! YET THESE ARE THE MISTY ISLES AND ALETA IS THEIR QUEEN!

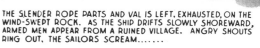

HAL FOSTER          NEXT WEEK-"Aleta"

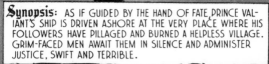
**Synopsis:** AS IF GUIDED BY THE HAND OF FATE, PRINCE VALIANT'S SHIP IS DRIVEN ASHORE AT THE VERY PLACE WHERE HIS FOLLOWERS HAVE PILLAGED AND BURNED A HELPLESS VILLAGE. GRIM-FACED MEN AWAIT THEM IN SILENCE AND ADMINISTER JUSTICE, SWIFT AND TERRIBLE.

WHEN NIGHT FALLS VAL SWIMS ASHORE FROM HIS HIDING-PLACE, WEAK WITH EXHAUSTION, SICK WITH HORROR.

AT DAWN A STRANGE PROCESSION PASSES THE PLACE WHERE HE LIES CONCEALED. AT INTERVALS THEY STOP AND ERECT GHASTLY WARNINGS TO FUTURE TRESPASSERS.

"WHAT FIENDS THESE ISLANDERS MUST BE TO TREAT MY FAITHFUL CREW IN THIS HORRIBLE MANNER!" VAL DOES NOT KNOW HOW RICHLY HIS MEN HAVE EARNED THIS FATE!

HE IS CAUTIOUSLY FOLLOWING THE SHORE LINE, SEARCHING FOR A BOAT, WHEN THE TINKLING OF A WATERFALL PROMISES A COOL DRINK. HE TURNS UP A PLEASANT VALLEY.

AT FIRST GLANCE THE WATERFALL SEEMS TO BE PURE GOLD.... THEN HE SEES IT IS A SLIM MAID WASHING HER FAIR HAIR.

SHE LOOKS UP, PUSHING THE GLEAMING HAIR FROM HER FACE. "ALETA!" GASPS VAL.

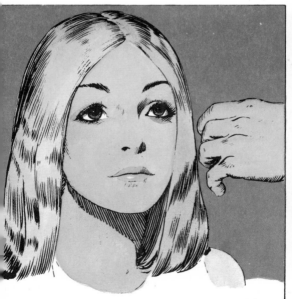

"FOR A FULL MINUTE SHE GAZES AT HIM FROM CALM GREY EYES. "I KNEW YOU WOULD RETURN, RASH BOY, DESPITE MY WARNING." AND HER VOICE TREMBLES EVER SO SLIGHTLY.

"YES, I HAVE RETURNED," HE CRIES, "ONLY TO FIND THE MISTY ISLES A PLACE OF CRUELTY AND TERROR; WHOSE PEOPLE KILL HORRIBLY THE HAPLESS STRANGERS....AND YOU!....YOU, THEIR QUEEN, MUST BE THE WORST OF ALL!"

251  11-30-41

AND VAL, HIS ROMANTIC DREAM SHATTERED, STUMBLES BACK THE WAY HE CAME, HEEDLESS OF DISCOVERY.

NEXT WEEK— **"You will never guess....."**

**Synopsis:** WEAK FROM HUNGER, DROOPING WITH WEARINESS, PRINCE VALIANT AT LAST MEETS ALETA, QUEEN OF THE MISTY ISLES. GLARING AT HER FROM BLOOD-SHOT EYES, HE BITTERLY UPBRAIDS HER FOR THE TERRIBLE FATE OF HIS CREW. HE DOES NOT KNOW WHAT SCOUNDRELS HIS SAILORS WERE OR HOW RICHLY THEY DESERVED THEIR PUNISHMENT.

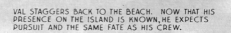

VAL STAGGERS BACK TO THE BEACH. NOW THAT HIS PRESENCE ON THE ISLAND IS KNOWN, HE EXPECTS PURSUIT AND THE SAME FATE AS HIS CREW.

ALETA CLIMBS A GRASSY KNOLL AND LONG SHE WATCHES THE RECKLESS YOUTH, AS HE WANDERS ALONG THE SHORE. THEN SHE CALLS HER HANDMAIDENS AND GIVES THEM CERTAIN ORDERS.

AFTER A SCANTY MEAL OF SHELL-FISH, HE CURLS UP IN A SHELTERED SPOT FOR THE NIGHT.

AT THE FIRST LIGHT OF DAWN VAL AWAKES TO MAKE A STARTLING DISCOVERY.... A SMALL SAIL BOAT HAS DRIFTED ASHORE RIGHT BEFORE HIS PLACE OF CONCEALMENT!

SPRINGING FROM HIS LAIR, HE WHIPS OUT HIS SWORD AND DASHES ACROSS THE BEACH.

BUT THE BOAT IS UNOCCUPIED AND HE SHOVES OFF HURRIEDLY. "I MAY YET ESCAPE FROM THIS PLACE OF HORROR AND CRUELTY!"

252 12-7-41

ONLY WHEN HE IS FAR FROM SHORE DOES HE EXAMINE THE BOAT AND ITS CONTENTS. IT IS FULLY PROVISIONED DOWN TO THE LAST DETAIL....AND THE LAST DETAIL IS A NOTE, WHICH READS:— "YOU MERIT PUNISHMENT FOR SPEAKING HARSH WORDS TO A QUEEN, IMPETUOUS YOUTH, BUT ONCE AGAIN I HELP YOU TO ESCAPE FROM THIS TROUBLED LAND. YOU WILL NEVER GUESS WHY!"
ALETA, QUEEN OF THE MISTY ISLES.

NEXT WEEK — **Athens and the Viking.**

HAL FOSTER

# Prince Valiant

ALETA
QUEEN OF THE MISTY ISLES

**Synopsis:** ONCE AGAIN PRINCE VALIANT SAILS AWAY FROM THE MISTY ISLES IN A BOAT PROVIDED BY QUEEN ALETA, BUT THIS TIME THERE IS NO WILD DESIRE TO RETURN, HE WISHES ONLY TO SAIL FAR AWAY FROM THAT CRUEL PLACE. THE FATE OF HIS CREW FILLS HIM WITH HORROR, FOR HE DOES NOT KNOW HIS MEN HAD EARNED THEIR DOOM.

HIS ROMANTIC DREAMS HAVE TURNED TO BITTERNESS. THERE SEEMS NO LONGER ANY PURPOSE TO HIS LIFE, ONLY A GREAT LONGING FOR HIS WINDY, NORTHERN HOME.

QUEEN ALETA WATCHES THE TINY SAIL UNTIL IT IS LOST IN THE IMMENSITY OF THE SEA, THEN SHE LIES FOR A LONG TIME FACE-DOWN IN THE GRASS AND HER SHOULDERS SHAKE. BUT WHETH-ER SHE LAUGHS OR WHETHER SHE CRIES, NO ONE CAN TELL. SHE IS YOUNG AND BEAUTIFUL AND QUEEN OF THE MISTY ISLES. WHY SHOULD SHE WEEP?

FOLLOWING THE TRACK OF PASSING MERCHANT VESSELS, VAL AT LAST COMES TO PIRAEUS, THE HARBOR OF ATHENS.

INTO THE BUSY PORT HE SAILS, THEN, DRESSED IN THE RAIMENT PROVIDED BY ALETA, HE STEPS ASHORE......

....AND THE FIRST PERSON HE SEES IS A SIX-FOOT VIKING, A STRANGE SIGHT EVEN IN THIS COSMOPOLITAN PORT!

VAL SPEAKS TO HIM IN HIS OWN TONGUE....THE VIKING'S FACE LIGHTS UP AND HE ROARS A GREETING!

253 12-14-41

HAL FOSTER

BY SHEER FORCE HE DRAGS VAL TO A WINE SHOP AND STRAIGHTWAY WIPES OUT THE MEMORY OF HIS LONELINESS WITH MUCH TALK AND MORE STRONG GRECIAN LIBATION!

NEXT WEEK— **The Viking Ship.**

**Synopsis:** WHEN PRINCE VALIANT ENTERS PIRAEUS, THE HARBOR OF ATHENS, THE FIRST PERSON HE SEES IS A TALL VIKING. VAL HAILS HIM IN HIS NATIVE TONGUE, WHICH SO PLEASES THE LONELY NORTHMAN THAT HE DRAGS VAL INTO A TAVERN FOR A LONG TALK

"I AM BOLTAR, THE VIKING, A RESPECTABLE PIRATE AND HONEST MERCHANT, BUT I CANNOT DO A PROFITABLE BUSINESS WITH THESE WILY GREEKS!"

"THE GREEKS ARE SMART, SHREWD, NIMBLE AND GOT THE BEST OF ME........ THEY HAVE PRACTICALLY DONE ME OUT OF MY RICH CARGO OF FURS!"
THE MORE INDIGNANT HE BECAME, THE MORE HE DRANK AND THE MORE HE DRANK, THE LOUDER BECAME HIS INDIGNATION.

VAL MARVELS AT HIS CAPACITY FOR BOTH.....IT IS DAWN BEFORE THE VIKING SLIDES QUIETLY FROM HIS CHAIR AND GOES PEACEFULLY TO SLEEP ON THE STONE FLOOR.

WHEN AT LAST BOLTAR AWAKES HIS HEAD ACHES AND HE FEELS VERY UNHAPPY INSIDE. HE WANTS THE FAMILIAR FEEL OF A DECK BENEATH HIS FEET AND INSISTS VAL COME WITH HIM.

HIS SHIP IS A SORRY SIGHT.....FOR HIS CREW ARE VIKINGS, WARRIORS ALL, WHO CAN EAT LIKE HORSES, DRINK LIKE FISH, FIGHT LIKE DEMONS AND DIE LIKE HEROES. AT THIS PARTICULAR TIME THEY LOOK LIKE DEAD FISH!

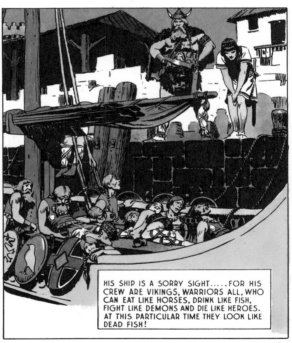

A ROAR FROM BOLTAR BRINGS THEM TO THEIR FEET. "PREPARE TO SAIL, YOU SODDEN SCOUNDRELS. FETCH THE CARGO!" IT IS A LARGE CARGO FOR A CHEATED MERCHANT TO BUY.

"JUST SOME STUFF WE PICKED UP," SAYS BOLTAR, WITH A GRIN, "MY MEN 'FIND' IT HERE AND THERE AND BRING IT ABOARD JUST BEFORE WE SAIL."

THERE IS MUCH ANGRY SHOUTING FROM THE TOWN, AS THEY SAIL AWAY. THOUGH VAL DOUBTS THE BOASTED HONESTY OF BOLTAR, HE SAILS WITH THEM.....FOR THIS SHIP IS BOUND FOR HIS DISTANT HOMELAND!

NEXT WEEK- **Homeward Bound.**

254  12-21-41

**Synopsis:** WHEN THE ROMANTIC QUEST TO FIND ALETA, QUEEN OF THE MISTY ISLES, ENDS IN DISAPPOINTMENT, PRINCE VALIANT LONGS FOR HIS COOL NORTHERN HOMELAND. HE TAKES PASSAGE WITH BOLTAR, AS BOISTEROUS A ROGUE AS EVER SAILED THE SEAS.

WESTWARD, EVER WESTWARD GLIDES THE TRIM SHIP OF BOLTAR, THE VIKING, AND HALF THE NAVIES OF THE WORLD WOULD LIKE TO LAY THIS WILY SCOUNDREL BY THE HEELS!

OCCASIONALLY THEY TOUCH AT SMALL VILLAGES AND FOR DRIED FRUIT AND FISH, HONEY, WINE AND MEAL BOLTAR PAYS GENEROUSLY..... AND THERE IS REJOICING.

NOW AND THEN THEY DO BUSINESS WITH PASSING MERCHANT SHIPS, BUT IN A DIFFERENT WAY...... AND THERE IS MUCH COMPLAINING.

AND ONCE, BECAUSE HIS ROVERS ARE SPOILING FOR A FIGHT, BOLTAR SACKS AND BURNS A FORTIFIED TOWN ON THE AFRICAN SHORE.....

THEY SAIL ON, WITH MUCH RICH LOOT AND MANY WOUNDS, BUT CALL IT A SUCCESSFUL BUSINESS TRANSACTION.

ONE DAY THE WIND BLEW FRESH AND COLD FROM OUT OF THE WEST, AND A HERD OF GIGANTIC WHALES GOES SURGING BY. THE VIKINGS SHOUT WITH JOY FOR THESE ARE SIGNS THAT THE OCEAN IS NOT FAR OFF.

THEN, IN THE DISTANCE THEY SEE THE GREAT PILLARS OF HERCULES THAT GUARD THE BLUE MEDITERRANEAN FROM THE GREY OCEAN. AND DRIFTING IN FROM THE ATLANTIC IS A BATTERED SHIP.

NEXT WEEK— **Rumor of Gold.**

HAL FOSTER

**Synopsis:** PRINCE VALIANT IS HOMEWARD BOUND ON THE SHIP OF BOLTAR, THE VIKING. BOLTAR HAS BEEN ON A TRADING VENTURE (WITH PIRACY AS A SIDE-LINE) AND, JUST AS THEY ARE LEAVING THE MEDITERRANEAN SEA, THEY MEET A BATTERED SHIP ENTERING FROM THE OCEAN.

BOLTAR STEERS ALONG-SIDE AND A STRANGE SIGHT MEETS THEIR EYES.

THE CREW, BOTH DEAD AND DYING, LIE SPRAWLED ABOUT THE DECK, WEAK FROM STARVATION AND FEVER. THE CAPTAIN SHUFFLES FORWARD, PLEADING FOR HELP.

BOLTAR RESPONDS MAGNIFICENTLY, FOR HIS SWASHBUCKLING FEROCITY IS EQUALED ONLY BY HIS GENEROSITY. THE CAPTAIN OFFERS, AS PAYMENT, A GREAT HANDFUL OF GOLDEN NUGGETS.

"WE HAVE A GREAT STORE OF GOLD, YOU MIGHT HAVE PLUNDERED US, FOR WE ARE TOO WEAK TO RESIST INSTEAD, YOU HELPED US AND IN RETURN I'LL SHOW YOU WHERE YOU, TOO, MAY OBTAIN THE CURSED METAL." AND HE DRAWS A CRUDE MAP.

"BRAVE FOLLOWERS," SAYS THE WILY BOLTAR WITH GREAT SADNESS, "IT IS TOO BAD WE ARE NORTHWARD BOUND, OUR HOMES ARE CALLING TO US AND WE MUST GO..... AND JUST WHEN I HAVE LEARNED THAT THERE IS GOLD BEYOND MEASURE TO THE SOUTH!"

WHEREUPON HE DIVIDES THE GOLD AND LETS EACH MAN HOLD HIS SHARE OF THE PRECIOUS METAL IN HIS HAND.

OUT OF THE STRAITS THEY SAIL INTO THE HEAVING OCEAN. "WHICH WAY SHALL WE TURN?" ASKS BOLTAR, "SOUTHWARD!" ROARS THE CREW. A LOOK OF SURPRISE COMES OVER BOLTAR'S INNOCENT FACE.

256 1-4-42

HAL FOSTER

VAL WATCHES THE NORTH STAR GETTING LOWER ON THE HORIZON AND WONDERS HOW LONG IT WILL BE BEFORE THEY ONCE MORE RAISE THAT SAME STAR OVER THEIR BOWS AND HEAD HOMEWARD TOWARD BRITAIN AND KING ARTHUR'S COURT.

NEXT WEEK— **Southward!**

**Synopsis:** PRINCE VALIANT TAKES PASSAGE WITH BOLTAR, THE VIKING, BOUND FOR THE NORTHLANDS AND THE COURT OF KING ARTHUR. WESTWARD ACROSS THE BLUE MEDITERRANEAN THEY SAIL, TRADING AND PLUNDERING MERRILY UNTIL THEY REACH THE PILLARS OF HERCULES (GIBRALTAR). THERE THEY HEAR RUMORS OF GOLD, AND, FORGETTING THEIR HOMES, THEY TURN SOUTH.

FAIR WINDS CARRY THEM UP THE COAST OF AFRICA. THEY SUFFER MUCH FROM THIRST, FOR THERE IS BUT LITTLE WATER ALONG THIS BURNING, SANDY COAST.

THEN ONE DAY THE WIND DIES, THE HEAT IS STIFLING AND OMINOUS CLOUDS GATHER OVER THE FAR SAHARA SANDS.

AS IF ALL THE SCREAMING FIENDS OF THE LOWER WORLD, THE STORM RUSHES DOWN UPON THEM. NO MAN CAN FACE THE WIND, FOR IT IS FILLED WITH STINGING SAND. THEIR MAST SNAPS LIKE A DRY REED!

ONE HALF THE CREW GRASP THE OARS AND STRIVE TO KEEP THE SHIP HEADED TO THE GALE. THE OTHERS BAIL LIKE MAD AND HEAVE THE BALLAST OVERBOARD

THEY ARE DRIVEN FAR OUT ON THE UNKNOWN OCEAN ERE THE STORM SPENDS ITSELF..........THEN, FAINTLY THROUGH THE STILL DUST-FILLED AIR, THEY SEE A SNOW-CAPPED MOUNTAIN RISING FROM THE SEA.

EAGERLY THEY PULL TOWARD THIS PROMISE OF REST AND FRESH WATER......

....BUT AS THEY BEACH THEIR SHIP, A PACK OF MONSTROUS DOGS LINES THE SHORE, FANGS GLEAMING.

THEY HAVE LANDED ON AN ISLAND PARADISE INHABITED BY DEMONS! AND THEIR SEARCH FOR WATER IS LIKE A HOWLING NIGHTMARE. BY ACCIDENT BOLTAR HAS RE-DISCOVERED THE "ISLE OF CANINES", OR AS THEY ARE NOW KNOWN, THE CANARY ISLANDS.

NEXT WEEK— **The Unknown Land.**

HAL FOSTER

257 1-11-42

Synopsis: PRINCE VALIANT IS SAILING FOR HIS HOMELAND WITH BOLTAR, THE VIKING, WHEN RUMORS OF GOLD SEND THEM COURSING SOUTHWARD UP THE COAST OF AFRICA. DRIVEN OUT TO SEA BY A STORM, THEY RE-DISCOVER THE "ISLE OF DOGS", NOW KNOWN AS THE CANARY ISLANDS.

HIGH ON THE MOUNTAIN SLOPES THEY FIND CEDAR, PINE AND OAK AND REPAIRS ARE MADE TO THEIR BATTERED SHIP. THEY FIND PLENTY OF WATER, FRUIT AND FISH IN THIS ISLAND PARADISE, BUT NO REST......

......FOR ONLY BY ETERNAL VIGILANCE CAN THEY KEEP OFF THE PACKS OF MONSTROUS DOGS THAT SWARM EVERYWHERE.

THEN THEY SAIL EASTWARD TO THE AFRICAN COAST AND AGAIN TURN SOUTH FOLLOWING THE TREELESS, DESERT WASTES.

GRADUALLY THE SHORE-LINE CHANGES, PALM TREES APPEAR AND MUDDY RIVERS. THE WIND FAILS AND THE HEAT BECOMES TERRIFIC. BOLTAR AND VAL TAKE THEIR TURN AT THE OARS. THEY HAVE REACHED THE DOLDRUMS.

THE COAST-LINE TURNS EASTWARD AND THEY ARE IN A LAND OF HEAT AND MUD. STRANGE TREES GROW IN THE SEA AND THE SEA FLOWS AMONG THE TREES. RIVERS, MUD AND SEA ARE ALL ONE.

A GREAT RIVER OPENS A PATHWAY THROUGH THE JUNGLELAND. AFTER STUDYING HIS CRUDE MAP CAREFULLY, BOLTAR ORDERS THEM TO ROW INLAND.....

Copr 1942, King Features Syndicate, Inc. World rights reserved.  258  1-18-42

...A WORLD OF CONTRASTS; SONS OF THE ICY NORTHLANDS ROW A VIKING SHIP THROUGH A STEAMING, FEVER-HAUNTED JUNGLE. HIDEOUS DRAGONS SQUIRM ON SLIMY MUDBANKS, WHILE GOR-GEOUS BIRDS GLIDE OVERHEAD. RIVER-MONSTERS AMONGST SWEET WATER-LILIES! BEAUTY AND HORROR EVERYWHERE!

NEXT WEEK- The Giant.

# Prince Valiant

IN THE DAYS OF KING ARTHUR
BY
HAROLD R FOSTER

**Synopsis:** WHEREVER THERE IS GOLD OR EVEN RUMOR OF GOLD, THERE MEN WILL GO, DESPITE ALL HARDSHIPS. SO THE SHIP OF BOLTAR. THE VIKING, GLIDES UP A JUNGLE RIVER IN UNKNOWN AFRICA AND PRINCE VALIANT IS A PASSENGER.

① ONLY THE DESIRE FOR GOLD KEEPS THESE HARDY ADVENTURERS FROM TURNING BACK. FOR THE JUNGLE IS A PLACE OF HORROR, WITH GREAT SERPENTS, DRAGONS. RIVER MONSTERS AND UNBEARABLE HEAT.

② ENEMIES THEY CAN NEITHER FIGHT NOR SEE ATTACK THEM. FIRST IT IS FEVER.

③ THEN FROM THE DENSE JUNGLE COMES A FLIGHT OF STINGING, POISONED DARTS; CAUSING FESTERING WOUNDS AND SOMETIMES DEATH.

④ ONE DAY THEY COME UPON A VILLAGE AND PREPARE TO MEET AN ENEMY FACE TO FACE AT LAST

⑤ BUT THE VILLAGE IS DESERTED. THEN A TERRIBLE THING HAPPENS, VAL, SEEING A MOVEMENT AMONG THE TREES. RUNS FORWARD.......

259 1-25-42

⑥ .......HE BURSTS THROUGH THE THICKET AND THERE, FACING HIM WITH BARED FANGS AND THE MALEVOLENT GLARE OF A DEMON, IS AN OGRE OF SUCH TERRIFYING ASPECT THAT VAL'S BRAVE HEART QUAILS WITHIN HIM.

NEXT WEEK— **The Battle**

HAL FOSTER

**Synopsis:** RUMORS OF GOLD SEND A VIKING CREW FAR UP A JUNGLE RIVER IN UNKNOWN AFRICA AND WITH THEM GOES PRINCE VALIANT. THEIR WAY IS BESET WITH DRAGONS (CROCODILES) SERPENTS (PYTHONS) AND GREAT RIVER MONSTERS (HIPPOS) AT LAST THEY REACH A DESERTED VILLAGE AND THERE, AT THE EDGE OF THE CLEARING, VAL MEETS A TERRIFYING OGRE.

THE MONSTER BEATS ITS CHEST AND A SOUND OF WAR-DRUMS ECHOES THROUGH THE JUNGLE. ITS FACE IS THE FACE OF A DEMON.

SLOWLY IT ADVANCES AND VAL GIVES GROUND, CALLING TO HIS COMPANIONS FOR AID.

THEN IT RUSHES....THE «SINGING SWORD» FLASHES DOWN, BUT THE MIGHTY STROKE ONLY WOUNDS AND INFURIATES THE MONSTER. IT SNATCHES AT VAL'S SHIELD AND FLINGS HIM, LIKE A WET RAG, INTO THE THICKET BEHIND.

THEN IT STRIDES AMONG THE DARTING SPEARS, SEIZES A WARRIOR AND LITERALLY TEARS HIM TO SHREDS.

WHEN FINALLY THE WOOD-DEMON FALLS, THE VIKINGS GATHER AROUND AND GAZE AT IT FEARFULLY. IT IS THE SIZE OF FOUR FULL-GROWN WARRIORS AND HAS THE STRENGTH OF TEN

THEN, FROM OUT THE JUNGLE COMES A BLACK MAN, CAUTIOUSLY. HE LAYS DOWN HIS WEAPONS, AS A SIGN OF PEACE. BY SIGNS HE THANKS THE VIKINGS FOR KILLING THE MONSTER.

A PARLEY IS HELD IN SIGN LANGUAGE. VAL SHOWS SOME GOLD AND INDICATES THEY WANT TO HAVE MORE. THE BLACK CHIEF SAYS THEY HAVE SOME...BUT HIS PEOPLE ARE STARVING, BECAUSE THE TERRIBLE WOOD-DEMONS EAT THEIR CROPS AND PREVENT THEIR HUNTING IN THE WOODS.

HAL FOSTER

A BARGAIN IS MADE. ALL THE GOLD TWO STRONG MEN CAN LIFT FOR VICTORY OVER THE WOOD-DEMONS. VAL SHOWS THE VIKINGS HOW TO CONSTRUCT SEVERAL SMALL MANGONELS.

NEXT WEEK — *The Battle of the Demons.*

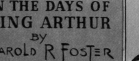
**Synopsis:** GOLD! WHO CAN RESIST ITS CALL? NOT BOLTAR, THE VIKING. FOR HE SAILS INTO THE UNKNOWN AND BRAVES THE DANGERS OF HEAT AND FEVER, POISONED ARROWS AND HIDEOUS MONSTERS AND TAKES PRINCE VALIANT ALONG WITH HIM. THEY SLAY A TERRIBLE WOOD-DEMON AND THE NATIVES PROMISE THEM ALL THE GOLD TWO STRONG MEN CAN LIFT, IF THE VIKINGS WILL VANQUISH THE WOOD-DEMONS.

VAL CONSTRUCTS SEVERAL MANGONELS AND SETS THEM UP IN THE FIELDS.

AT DUSK HUGE SHAPES CAN BE SEEN MOVING AT THE EDGE OF THE JUNGLE. THEN THEY ADVANCE, SUPPORTING THEIR HUGE BODIES ON POWERFUL ARMS.

ON THEY COME, DEVOURING THE CROPS, UNHEEDING THE PUNY HUMANS WHO HAVE NEVER BEEN ABLE TO FACE THEM. THE MANGONELS TWANG!

THE CHARGE OF THE WOOD-DEMONS IS TERRIBLE, MANY FALL, AND THOUGH VICTORY IS WITH THE VIKINGS, IT IS NOT WITHOUT COST.

FOR THE FIRST TIME MEN HAVE FACED THE HAIRY OGRES OF THE FORESTS SUCCESSFULLY. RELENTLESSLY, THE VIKINGS HUNT THEM DOWN.

THEN COMES THE GOOD NEWS; A NATIVE SCOUT HAS SEEN THE MONSTERS ALL BANDED TOGETHER AND MOVING AWAY TO SOME OTHER MORE QUIET REGION.

THE DAY OF PAYMENT HAS ARRIVED, BUT THERE IS NOT SUFFICIENT GOLD TO SATISFY BOLTAR! THE BLACK CHIEF SENDS A CANOE UPSTREAM FOR MORE.

261 2-8-42

HAL FOSTER

BOLTAR SAYS, *"PRINCE VALIANT, TAKE THE SMALL BOAT, FOLLOW THAT CANOE AND SEE WHERE THEY GET THE GOLD."*
NEXT WEEK— **Jungle Terrors.**

Synopsis: FAR UP A JUNGLE RIVER, BOLTAR AND HIS VIKING CREW RESCUE A NATIVE TRIBE...FOR A PRICE...AND THE PRICE IS ALL THE GOLD TWO STRONG MEN CAN LIFT! A CANOE IS SENT UPSTREAM TO FETCH MORE AND BOLTAR SENDS PRINCE VALIANT TO DISCOVER WHERE THE GOLD COMES FROM.

FOR SEVERAL DAYS THEY FOLLOW IN THE WAKE OF THE SWIFT CANOE. THE RIVER NARROWS AND THE HEAT IS ALMOST UNBEARABLE.

GRADUALLY THE COUNTRY CHANGES, THE WATER IS LESS MUDDY, FALLS AND RAPIDS ARE ENCOUNTERED. HILLS APPEAR ON EITHER SIDE

A PATH LEADS UP FROM THE RIVER AND HERE THEY FIND THE CANOE THEY HAVE BEEN FOLLOWING. HIDING THE BOAT, VAL LEADS THE WAY UPWARD.

FEARFUL DANGERS CONFRONT THEM, ONCE THEY ARE CHARGED BY A UNICORN AND A WARRIOR IS KILLED.

WHILE MAKING CAMP AT A WATER-HOLE, A MONSTROUS SERPENT REARS ITS HEAD HIGH ABOVE THE TREE TOPS AND THEY WOULD HAVE FLED IN PANIC. BUT THEY FEAR THE JUNGLE AT NIGHT

262  2-15-42

DAWN COMES AT LAST... AND WITH IT THEIR GREATEST TERROR. A VAST SHADOW LOOMS OVER THEM AND LOOKING UP, THEY BEHOLD A MONSTER SO HUGE IT SEEMS UNFAIR TO HUMANS. THEY FLEE DOWN THE PATH WHENCE THEY CAME!

NEXT WEEK— Homeward!

HAL FOSTER

# Prince Valiant
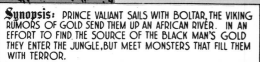

IN THE DAYS OF
KING ARTHUR
BY
HAROLD R FOSTER

ALETA
QUEEN OF THE MISTY ISLES

**Synopsis:** PRINCE VALIANT SAILS WITH BOLTAR, THE VIKING RUMORS OF GOLD SEND THEM UP AN AFRICAN RIVER. IN AN EFFORT TO FIND THE SOURCE OF THE BLACK MAN'S GOLD THEY ENTER THE JUNGLE, BUT MEET MONSTERS THAT FILL THEM WITH TERROR.

SUCH A DRAGON THEY HAD NEVER EVEN IMAGINED. WITHOUT A WORD, THE VIKINGS FLEE TO THEIR BOAT.

RECKLESS WITH FEAR, THEY HURRY FROM THE ACCURSED PLACE.

VAL HEAVES A GREAT SIGH OF RELIEF, WHEN ONCE AGAIN HE AND HIS COMPANIONS ARE ABOARD THE FAMILIAR SHIP.

TWO DAYS LATER THE NATIVES RETURN, THEIR CANOE WELL-LOADED AND A GREAT FEAST IS PREPARED, FOR THESE STRANGE, WHITE MEN HAVE SAVED THEIR TRIBE FROM THE WOOD-DEMONS.

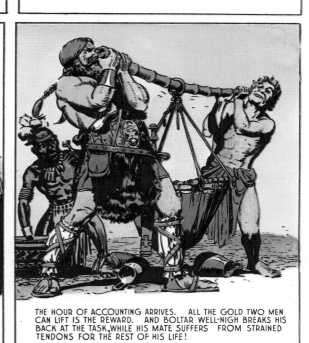

THE HOUR OF ACCOUNTING ARRIVES. ALL THE GOLD TWO MEN CAN LIFT IS THE REWARD. AND BOLTAR WELL-NIGH BREAKS HIS BACK AT THE TASK, WHILE HIS MATE SUFFERS FROM STRAINED TENDONS FOR THE REST OF HIS LIFE!

HOMEWARD NOW! AND THE OARS FLASH IN THE BURNING SUNLIGHT, AS THEY FLEE PAST THE DRAGONS AND WATER MONSTERS TOWARD THE OPEN SEA!

NOR DO THEY SLOW DOWN AT THE RIVER-MOUTH, BUT KEEP RIGHT ON UNTIL THEY ARE FAR OUT TO SEA. THEN THE ROVERS FILL THEIR LUNGS WITH THE KEEN SEA AIR AND THE WOUNDED, SICK AND FEVER-WRACKED CRAWL ON DECK AND KNOW THAT THEY WILL LIVE AGAIN!

NEXT WEEK— **The Prisoner.**

263 2-22-42

**Synopsis:** OUT OF THE STEAMING JUNGLE COMES THE SHIP OF BOLTAR AND HIS VIKINGS WITH A CARGO OF FEVER, GOLD AND WOUNDS....REJOICING, FOR THEY ARE LEAVING TERROR AND DANGER BEHIND. THEY TURN WESTWARD, FOLLOWING THE AFRICAN COAST.

DAY AFTER DAY THEY PULL OVER A GLASSY OCEAN UNDER A BURNING SKY.

AT LAST THE COAST TURNS NORTHWARD AND THEY ARE HOMEWARD BOUND! THEY STRAIN AT THE OARS WITH NEVER A FAIR WIND. DAYS TURN INTO WEEKS, A MONTH GOES BY.......

THEN OFF CAPE FINISTERRE THEY PICK UP THE "WESTERLIES," SPREAD THEIR LEATHERN SAILS AND GO FOAMING ACROSS BISCAY.

THERE IS SNOW IN THE AIR, ICE FORMS IN THE RIGGING AND THE VIKINGS DON THEIR FURS AND COWER IN THE SHELTER OF THE BULWARKS. NOW THIS IS MORE TO THEIR LIKING!

THEY SAIL INTO A SEAPORT IN GAUL FOR SUPPLIES AND REPAIRS. A FROWNING CASTLE DOMINATES THE TOWN.

BOLTAR SOON DISPATCHES HIS BUSINESS IN THE TOWN THEN, ARM IN ARM WITH PRINCE VALIANT, SWAGGERS TO THE NEAREST TAVERN.

HERE A YOUNG COURTIER FROM THE CASTLE COMES TO THEM AND OFFERS A PURSE OF GOLD, IF THEY WILL CARRY A LETTER ACROSS THE CHANNEL TO BRITAIN.

*"CERTAINLY, GIVE ME THE PURSE!"* CRIES BOLTAR. THEN AS SOON AS THE YOUNG MAN HAD LEFT, RIPS OPEN THE LETTER. *"HERE, VAL, READ WHAT IT SAYS, FOR I DISTRUST WRITING."*

HAL FOSTER

VAL LEAPS TO HIS FEET WITH AN OATH! *"IT IS A DEMAND FOR RANSOM! MY FRIEND, SIR GAWAIN, IS HELD PRISONER IN THE DUNGEON OF YONDER CASTLE!"*

NEXT WEEK — **A Voice from the Past.**

**Synopsis:** "BOLTAR, THE VIKING," AND HIS FRIEND, PRINCE VALIANT, ARE RETURNING HOME WITH A CARGO OF GOLD AND THE REMAINDER OF THEIR CREW, WHEN THEY INTERCEPT A RANSOM LETTER. SIR GAWAIN IS BEING HELD PRISONER IN A NEARBY CASTLE!

"FOR THE FIRST TIME IN MONTHS, WE CAN DRINK OUR FILL OF GOOD VINTAGES," MOANS BOLTAR. "AND THEN, THIS HAS TO HAPPEN!"

VAL STRIDES UP THE VILLAGE STREET TO THE CASTLE GATE AND SOUNDS A LOUD BLAST UPON THE HORN ATTACHED THERETO.

THE GATES ARE UNBARRED AND VAL STORMS IN. "SHOW ME TO YOUR MASTER, QUICKLY!"

GUY HAAKON LOOKS UP FROM HIS SUPPER IMPATIENTLY. "WHAT DO YOU WANT, VARLET?" "I COME TO RANSOM MY FRIEND, SIR GAWAIN!"

"WHY, YOU RAGGED YOKEL! ONE PENNY WOULD BE A FORTUNE TO YOU." AND HAAKON LAUGHS CONTEMPTUOUSLY.

THEN HE STOPS LAUGHING QUICKLY. FOR PRINCE VALIANT IS NOT THE KIND OF YOUTH PEOPLE LAUGH AT WHEN ANGER SMOLDERS IN HIS RECKLESS EYES.

"FIRST, I MUST BE SURE IT IS SIR GAWAIN, FOR I TRUST YOU NOT. HAVE YOUR SERVANT SAY TO HIM, "HOW LONG DID YOU STAY IN ROME WITH PRINCE VALIANT?"

THE ANSWER IS TYPICAL OF GAWAIN: "SIR, THE PRISONER SAYS: 'LONG ENOUGH FOR TWO SPLENDID FIGHTS AND A MOST DELIGHTFUL LOVE AFFAIR'. HE ALSO SAID SOME INSULTING THINGS ABOUT THE MASTER, WHICH I CANNOT REPEAT".

265  3-8-42

VAL STRAIGHTWAY RETURNS TO BOLTAR. "GIVE ME MY SHARE OF THE GOLD, NOW!"

NEXT WEEK — **The Ransoming of Sir Gawain.**

**Synopsis:** TO PAY SIR GAWAIN'S RANSOM PRINCE VALIANT DEMANDS HIS SHARE OF GOLD FROM BOLTAR. "BUT, VAL, IT TOOK MONTHS OF HARDSHIP AND DANGER TO WIN THIS GOLD! YOU WILL BE A PAUPER!

"I HAVE YOUTH AND HEALTH . . . AND NOT ENOUGH SENSE TO WORRY WITH! WHAT MORE DO I NEED? BESIDES, GAWAIN IS MY FRIEND!"

"I WILL GATHER THE CREW AND WE'LL FREE YOUR FRIEND BY FORCE OF ARMS! "NO," SAYS VAL FIRMLY, "I'VE SEEN THE CASTLE, IT IS TOO STRONG FOR ASSAULT."

WHEN VAL HAS GONE HIS INDEPENDENT WAY, BOLTAR WHISPERS TO HIS CREW. THEY PICK UP ODDS AND ENDS OF CUTLERY, TIGHTEN THEIR BELTS AND SMILE GRIMLY TO THEMSELVES.

A PRICE IS PAID, A BARGAIN MADE AND TWO FRIENDS GREET EACH OTHER ONCE AGAIN!

"NO MATTER WHAT YOU PAID FOR ME, VAL, I THINK YOU GOT A BAR-GAIN!" "PAYING ANY RANSOM FOR YOU," CORRECTS VAL, "IS LIKE PUTTING AN EIGHTY-TALENT (DOLLAR) SADDLE ON A TWENTY-TALENT HORSE!"

GUY HAAKON, FONDLING THE GOLD, GETS ANOTHER IDEA. "SOLDIERS, BRING THOSE TWO BACK, I'LL RANSOM THEM AGAIN, THIS TIME TO THEIR FAMILIES!"

BOLTAR MUST HAVE SUSPECTED SUCH A MOVE. FOR HE AND HIS MEN ARE THERE, AS THE SOLDIERS GALLOP FROM THE CASTLE IN THE GATHERING DUSK.

VAL AND GAWAIN SEE THEM COMING AND TAKE TO THEIR HEELS.

266 3-15-42

BOLTAR AND HIS VIKINGS ENTER THE GATE AND CLOSE IT BEHIND THEM. I'VE OFTEN WONDERED WHAT HAPPENED THEREAFTER; THE STORY NEVER TOLD.

NEXT WEEK — Vagabonds.

HAL FOSTER

**Synopsis:** PRINCE VALIANT GIVES ALL HIS HARD-EARNED STORE OF GOLD TO RANSOM SIR GAWAIN FROM THE HANDS OF GUY HAAKON. AND THEN HAAKON SENDS HIS HORSEMEN OUT TO RECAPTURE THEM AND THE TWO FRIENDS PLAY HIDE AND SEEK ALL NIGHT.

THEY TRY TO REACH THE SHIP OF BOLTAR, THE VIKING, BUT ALWAYS THE SOLDIERS OF HAAKON ARE BETWEEN THEM AND ESCAPE

DAWN COMES, AND FROM A DISTANT HILL-TOP THEY LOOK DOWN UPON THE TOWN. BOLTAR HAS GIVEN THEM UP AND IS SAILING AWAY AND FROM HAAKON'S CASTLE RISES A GREAT PILLAR OF SMOKE.

AFTER THREE MONTHS IN A DUNGEON CELL, THIS FREEDOM IS LIKE HEADY WINE TO SIR GAWAIN. HE SINGS, HE SHOUTS, HE JOKES AND LAUGHS FOR SHEER JOY!

"OWING TO YOUR LATE EXTRAVAGANCE, VAL, WE HAVE NO MONEY, I AM HUNGRY. I NEED A HORSE. BUT LOOK, A WEALTHY LADY APPROACHES. WATCH ME GO TO WORK!"

"PRINCESS ILDA!" WHISPERS GAWAIN, HIS VOICE HOARSE WITH EMOTION. "ILDA OF CARCASSON! YOUR HAUNTING BEAUTY ENSNARED MY HEART WHEN FIRST I SAW YOU AND I'VE SEARCHED THE WIDE WORLD OVER TO FIND YOU ONCE AGAIN!"

"BUT I AM NOT PRINCESS ILDA OF CARCASSON," SAYS THE PLEASED, PLUMP DAME. "WHAT!" EXCLAIMS GAWAIN STAGGERING BACK, "CAN IT BE POSSIBLE THAT TWO GIRLS CAN HAVE THE SAME LOVELY FACE THE SAME GRACE, CHARM AND DELICATE COLORING?"

"PARDON ME, O, MOST BEAUTIFUL LADY," MUTTERS GAWAIN, LIMP WITH DESPAIR. "THE HARDSHIPS, THE PRIVATIONS, THE HUNGER OF MY LONG SEARCH HAVE RENDERED ME STUPID. BUT THE RESEMBLANCE...!"

"SILLY BOY, I AM BUT DAME GILBERT. FANCY TAKING POOR PLAIN LITTLE ME FOR PRINCESS ILDA!" SAYS THE GOOD DAME POSITIVELY SIMPERING WITH PLEASURE. "HUGH! ALFRED! DISMOUNT AND LET THESE TWO POOR, TIRED GENTLEMEN HAVE YOUR HORSES!"

267 3-22-42

"YOU MUST BE WEARY, COLD AND HUNGRY, AFTER ALL YOUR SEARCHING ABOUT. YOU WILL SIMPLY HAVE TO COME HOME WITH ME AND REST AWHILE. WAS ILDA REALLY VERY BEAUTIFUL?"

NEXT WEEK— **My Kingdom for a Horse.**

HAL FOSTER

**Synopsis:** PRINCE VALIANT HAS JUST RANSOMED THE IMPRISONED SIR GAWAIN, PENNILESS AND AFOOT, THEY ENCOUNTER DAME GILBERT AND GAWAIN. WITH GLIB TONGUE AND OUTRAGEOUS FLATTERY SO PLEASES HER THAT SHE INVITES THEM HOME

THE GILBERT HOME IS LARGE AND LOOKS PLEASINGLY WEALTHY

SQUIRE GILBERT IS NOT OVERLY PLEASED. HIS WIFE SEEMS BEWITCHED. HIS HANDSOME VISITORS HAVE TERRIFIC APPETITES. THEY HAVE MADE THEMSELVES TOO MUCH AT HOME. THEY SAY NOTHING ABOUT LEAVING.

"GAWAIN, YOU ARE A CLOWN, A KNAVE, AND YOU HAVE DELUDED THAT POOR, SILLY, KINDLY WOMAN INTO GIVING US BOARD AND LODGING." "BUT I MUST HAVE A HORSE, TOO," GRINS GAWAIN.

"FAIREST LADY, I MUST LEAVE YOU, EVEN THOUGH I HAVE NO HORSE AND MUST TRUDGE AFOOT THROUGH SLUSH AND ICY MUD. I CAN NO LONGER GAZE UPON YOUR BEAUTY UNMOVED. IT IS BEST THAT I GO! AT LEAST IN A DAY OR SO."

"YES, YES, I'LL GET THEM HORSES! NOW STOP BEDEVILING ME. I'LL DO ANYTHING TO GET THEM TO GO, BEFORE THEY EAT ME OUT OF HOUSE AND HOME!"

NEXT MORNING TWO SPLENDID MOUNTS ARE TETHERED IN THE YARD. "HURRAH!" CALLS GAWAIN, "NOW WE WILL BE ON OUR WAY.. RIGHT AFTER BREAKFAST!"

"YOUR HORSES, ALL SADDLED AND BRIDLED, AWAIT YOU WITHOUT!" WITH A PROFUSION OF BOWING AND SMILING AND EXPRESSIONS OF GRATITUDE THEY DEPART AND THE DOOR CLOSES FIRMLY BEHIND THEM.

FOR A LONG TIME THEY STAND GAZING WITH SHOCKED SURPRISE. "EITHER SOME TERRIBLE CALAMITY HAS SUDDENLY OVERTAKEN THOSE SPLENDID MOUNTS OR SQUIRE GILBERT IS HAVING THE LAST LAUGH!"

HAL FOSTER

268 3-29-42

Copr. 1942 King Features Syndicate, Inc., World rights reserved

NEXT WEEK— **Jolly Sir Hubert.**

**Synopsis:** TWO PENNILESS VAGABONDS, PRINCE VALIANT AND SIR GAWAIN, TRUDGE THROUGH THE SLUSH AND MUD OF GAUL BOUND FOR ENGLAND AND KING ARTHUR'S COURT. THEY MEET A WEALTHY DAME AND, BY DINT OF A LITTLE LOVE-MAKING AND FLATTERY, SIR GAWAIN OBTAINS TWO HORSES......

...... BUT WHAT HORSES!

THE GALLANT SIR GAWAIN, THAT MOST RECKLESS OF HORSEMEN, HAS AT LAST FOUND A STEED HE CANNOT MASTER. HIS LANGUAGE IS BOTH VIVID AND PICTURESQUE!

AND HE IS IN NO MOOD FOR JESTING WHEN A VOICE BOOMS OUT:— *"CROWS, COME HITHER! YOUR DINNER IS SERVED!"*

*"I'LL MAKE CROW'S MEAT OUT OF YOU, JESTER!"* SNAPS GAWAIN. *"AS I LIVE AND WHEEZE, TWO FIGHTING MEN!"* EXCLAIMS THE FAT STRANGER, *"AND HUNGRY ONES, TOO, I'LL WAGER!"*

WHEREUPON THE JOLLY FELLOW INVITES THEM INTO HIS NEARBY CASTLE TO BE HIS GUESTS.

WITHIN THE COURTYARD IS GREAT TURMOIL. SERFS AND YEOMEN WORK FRANTICALLY, AS IF IN PREPARATION FOR IMMEDIATE ATTACK.

HARDLY HAVE THEY DISMOUNTED WHEN A HUGE ROCK COMES CRASHING OVER THE WALL. *"DEAR ME!"* SAYS THEIR HOST, *"HOW IMPULSIVE MY ENEMIES ARE.... AND JUST AT SUPPER-TIME, TOO."*

269 4-5-42

*"IS IT POSSIBLE YOU INVITED US HERE IN THE HOPE WE WOULD HELP YOU IN A NEIGHBORHOOD QUARREL?"* ASKS VAL. SIR HUBERT ONLY GRINS.

HAL FOSTER

*"YOU SEE,"* HE SAYS LATER, PRESENTING HIS YOUNG DAUGHTER, *"I HAVE TREASURES THAT MUST BE PROTECTED BY ANY MEANS THAT COME TO HAND."*

NEXT WEEK— **The Siege.**

# Prince Valiant

### IN THE DAYS OF KING ARTHUR
### BY HAROLD R FOSTER

SIR GAWAIN

**Synopsis:** SIR GAWAIN AND PRINCE VALIANT ACCEPT A DINNER INVITATION FROM SIR HUBERT. THE CASTLE IS ATTACKED AND SIR HUBERT ADMITS THEY WERE INVITED IN THE HOPE THEY WOULD AID HIM AGAINST HIS ENEMY, HUGH D'ARCY.

"TWAS NOT A KNIGHTLY TRICK, BUT MY DAUGHTER, CLAIR, IS THE PRIZE D'ARCY SEEKS AND I WILL PROTECT HER AT ANY COST."

FROM A TOWER THEY SCAN THE ENEMY PREPARATIONS TO JUDGE HOW BEST TO MEET THE ASSAULT.

OFTEN HAVE HUBERT AND D'ARCY LAID WASTE EACH OTHER'S DOMAINS, BUT THIS TIME D'ARCY HAS ASSEMBLED A GREAT FORCE OF MEN AND WAR MACHINES TO SETTLE THEIR ANCIENT FEUD FOR ALL TIME.

THE FIRST ASSAULT COMES LIKE A RAGING TIDE AND LIFE IS WASTED EXTRAVAGANTLY ERE IT EBBS.

THEN THE MACHINES ROLL UP AND GREAT ROCKS CRASH AGAINST THE WALLS, HOUR AFTER HOUR, DAY AFTER DAY.

THE WALL CRUMBLES, BUT SIR HUBERT, GAWAIN AND VAL STAND SHIELD TO SHIELD IN THE BREECH AND TALES WERE TOLD LONG AFTERWARD OF THEIR DEEDS THAT CRIMSON DAY.

FROM A TURRET WINDOW CLAIR STRAINS ANXIOUS EYES TOWARD THE FOE, LOOKING, SEARCHING FOR ONE PARTICULAR ENEMY.

THE MOST DIFFICULT FEAT THAT DAY WAS PERFORMED BY RAOUL, NEPHEW OF D'ARCY. HE LEFT HIS BODY WITH HIS UNCLE, BUT SENT HIS HEART INTO THE CASTLE.

270 4-12-42   Copr. 1942, King Features Synd. etc, Inc., World rights reserved.

THE BREECH IS CLOSED, BUT ERE THEY CLIMB TO SAFETY THEY SHOUT THEIR BATTLE-CRIES DEFIANTLY ... AND THE NAME PRINCE VALIANT CRIES IS: "ALETA!"

NEXT WEEK— **The Tryst.**

Synopsis: WHILE SIR GAWAIN AND PRINCE VALIANT ARE GUESTS OF SIR HUBERT, THE CASTLE IS BESIEGED BY HIS OLD ENEMY, HUGH D'ARCY, AND IN THE THICK OF THE FIGHT VAL FINDS HE IS SHOUTING, AS A BATTLE-CRY:— "ALETA!"

THOUGH WEARY AND BRUISED VAL CANNOT SLEEP. "WHY SHOULD I CRY HER HATED NAME? WHY CANNOT I FORGET HER LOVELY, CRUEL FACE?"

AT DAWN VAL SURPRISES CLAIR ANXIOUSLY SCANNING THE ENEMY LINES. "GO BELOW, CHILD. WATCHING THE FOE IS A JOB FOR ARMORED MEN ONLY."

D'ARCY STRIKES QUICK BLOWS FROM ALL SIDES, CARELESS OF HIS LOSSES AND BIT BY BIT, THE DEFENDERS ARE WHITTLED DOWN.

DEATH HOVERS ABOVE THE CASTLE, HEEDLESS OF WHOM IT PICKS AND YOUNG RAOUL D'ARCY IS FRANTIC WITH ANXIETY.

HE CAN STAND THE SUSPENSE NO LONGER. HE SWIMS THE MOAT AND THROWS HIS GRAPPLE OVER THE BATTLEMENTS.

PRINCE VALIANT IS TAKING HIS EASE IN A QUIET CORNER WHEN THE GRAPPLE COMES OVER.

HE FASTENS IT IN AN EMBRASURE AND WAITS. IT IS NOT A NIGHT ATTACK, FOR BUT ONE SOLITARY FIGURE CLIMBS UPWARD.

AS THE DRIPPING FIGURE STEPS UPON THE ROOF, HE IS SEIZED IN A GRIP THAT WELL-NIGH CRACKS HIS SPINE!

271 4-19-42    Copr. 1942, King Features Syndicate, Inc., World rights reserved.

"I YIELD!" GASPS RAOUL, "BUT BEFORE I DIE, TELL ME, IS CLAIR ALIVE AND UNHURT?"

HAL FOSTER

NEXT WEEK— The Romeo.

*Synopsis:* FOR WEEKS THE CASTLE OF SIR HUBERT HAS HELD OUT AGAINST THE FIERCE ASSAULT OF HUGH D'ARCY. THE PRIZE D'ARCY SEEKS, IS CLAIR, YOUNG DAUGHTER OF SIR HUBERT. HUGH'S NEPHEW, RAOUL D'ARCY, LOST HIS HEART AND FOLLOWS IT INTO THE ENEMY STRONGHOLD.

*"RECKLESS FOOL!"* CRIES VAL, *"DO YOU MEAN TO TELL ME YOU'VE RISKED YOUR SILLY NECK JUST TO INQUIRE ABOUT A GIRL'S HEALTH?"*

*"WHENEVER A MAN MAKES A SPLENDID FOOL OF HIMSELF, IT IS ALWAYS FOR SOME WOMAN!"* SAYS VAL BITTERLY WITH ALL THE VAST WISDOM OF EIGHTEEN YEARS.

*"YOU ARE MY PRISONER AND I MUST LOCK YOU IN THIS ROOM, BUT IF YOU LOOK FROM YONDER WINDOW, YOU'LL SEE CLAIR ON THE BATTLEMENTS, RISKING HER LIFE LOOKING FOR YOU!"*

AND NOW THE DEFENDERS FIGHT DESPERATELY, AS THEIR NUMBER GETS FEWER. IN THE DISTANCE VAL SEES D'ARCY BUILDING A BATTERING-RAM; A FINAL ASSAULT WILL BE MADE UPON THE GATE!

A COUNCIL IS CALLED. *"WE ARE GREATLY OUTNUMBERED. IN THIS FINAL ATTACK D'ARCY WILL ASSUREDLY WIN, BUT"*.... AND VAL GRINS.... *"I HAVE A PLAN!"*

A WALL IS BUILT, ENCLOSING A SPACE WITH BUT ONE OUTLET, THE GATE.

A SWINGING GATE OF STAUNCH TIMBERS IS HUNG ABOVE THE ORIGINAL DOOR, WHICH IS ALREADY CRUMBLING BENEATH THE ASSAULT.

272 4-26-42

*"NOW YOU, SIR HUBERT, MUST DELIVER THIS LOAD OF ROCK TO D'ARCY, AS HE PASSES THROUGH THE GATEWAY."* *"I SHALL NOT MISS,"* CHUCKLES THE OLD KNIGHT.

NEXT WEEK— The Last Assault.

**Synopsis:** SIR HUBERT HAS HELD OUT FOR WEEKS AGAINST THE ASSAULTS OF HIS OLD ENEMY, HUGH D'ARCY, BUT NOW HIS FORCES ARE SO WEAKENED THAT ONLY A MIRACLE CAN SAVE THE DAY.....OR ONE OF PRINCE VALIANT'S TRICKS.

① A STORM OF SCREAMING ARROWS KEEPS THE DEFENDERS UNDER COVER, WHILE THE BATTERING-RAM IS WHEELED UP.

② ABOVE THE ROAR OF BATTLE CAN BE HEARD THE RAM'S RHYTHMIC THUD. THEN, WITH A SPLINTERING CRASH, THE GATE GIVES WAY!

③ "FORWARD TO THE ASSAULT!" SCREAMS HUGH D'ARCY, "AND SPARE NO ONE!"

④ THROUGH THE BROKEN GATEWAY POUR THE YELLING SOLDIERS.

⑤ SIR HURBERT WAITS PATIENTLY UNTIL D'ARCY IS JUST BENEATH HIM, THEN DELIVERS HIS CART-LOAD OF BUILDING MATERIAL.

THE AMAZED AND LEADERLESS INVADERS FIND THEMSELVES IN A CUL-DE-SAC. THEN THE NEW GATE SWINGS DOWNWARD, HEAVY TIMBERS SHOOT ACROSS AND ANCHOR IT FIRMLY AND THEY ARE IN A PRISON. NO CHOICE IS LEFT THEM EXCEPT SURRENDER!

NEXT WEEK— **The New Lord of D'Arcy Hall**

⑥ 273 5-3-42

HAL FOSTER

**Synopsis:** SIR HUBERT HELD OFF THE SUPERIOR FORCES OF HUGH D'ARCY FOR WEEKS UNTIL AT LAST THEY BROKE THROUGH, SWARMED IN AND, THANKS TO PRINCE VALIANT'S LITTLE TRICK, FOUND THEM-SELVES PRISONERS. HUGH D'ARCY WAS, YOU MIGHT SAY, 'PURGED!'

"THROW YOUR WEAPONS TO MY ARCHERS UPON THE WALLS," CALLS SIR HUBERT IN A JOVIAL MOOD, "ELSE ALL YOUR WIVES WILL BE WIDOWS THIS NIGHT!"

"THANKS! THANKS! THANKS!" HE BELLOWS, "TO THE RIGHT ARM OF SIR GAWAIN AND THE WIT OF SIR VALIANT I OWE THE FACT THAT I AM NOW MASTER OF MY OWN DOMAIN AND D'ARCY HALL TOO, BY RIGHT OF CONQUEST!"

"NOT SO FAST, SIR HUBERT, D'ARCY'S NEPHEW, RAOUL, IS RIGHTFUL HEIR TO D'ARCY HALL."

"WHAT! THAT SIMPERING KNAVE WHO MAKES THE NIGHT HIDEOUS BY SINGING BENEATH MY DAUGHTER'S WINDOW! THAT FAINT-WIT WHO BESIEGES HER WITH SILLY SON-NETS AND FOOLISH LOVE-MAKING!.... AND HE SPUTTERS INTO WRATHFUL SILENCE.

FROM HIS CELL WINDOW RAOUL HAD WITNESSED HIS UNCLE'S DEFEAT AND EXPECTED NOTHING LESS THAN EXECUTION, AS WAS THE CUSTOM.

CLAIR, TOO, MUST HAVE THOUGHT THE SAME THING FOR SHE APPEARS SUDDENLY AND THE AGONY IN HER HEART SHOWS IN HER EYES.

"NOW, SIR HUBERT, YOU SOFT-HEARTED OLD ROUGE, ORDER RAOUL'S EXECUTION.....I DARE YOU!"

274 5-10-42

"SUCH A DAY!" GRUMBLES SIR HUBERT, "I WIN A BATTLE AND LOSE THE SPOILS OF WAR AND MY DAUGHTER TOO!" BUT THE HAPPINESS IN HIS EYES BELIE THE ANGER IN HIS VOICE.
"O WELL," HE CONTINUES MORE OPTIMISTICALLY, "CLAIR IS VERY MUCH LIKE HER MOTHER AND THIS D'ARCY STRIPLING WILL NOT, HEREAFTER, HAVE SUFFICIENT PEACE AND QUIET IN WHICH TO RENEW THE OLD FEUD."

NEXT WEEK— **Wedding Bells.**

HAL FOSTER

**Synopsis:** DUE TO PRINCE VALIANT'S STRATEGY THE SIEGE HAD A HAPPY ENDING, AT LEAST FOR THOSE FORTUNATE ENOUGH TO SURVIVE. GRIM HUGH D'ARCY FINDS PEACE AT LAST UNDER A LOAD OF ROCK AND RAOUL, THE LAST OF THE D'ARCYS IS RENDERED HELPLESS, USELESS AND A BIT SILLY BY THE BRIGHT EYES OF CLAIR, HIS ENEMY'S DAUGHTER.

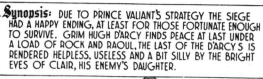

SIR HUBERT IS SO PLEASED THAT HE NOT ONLY REFUSES TO SLAUGHTER HIS PRISONERS BUT ALLOWS THE GRATEFUL FELLOWS (WITH BUT LITTLE PERSUASION) TO REBUILD HIS BATTERED CASTLE!

THEN THE WEDDING FEAST IS HELD IN THE GREAT HALL. LONG AFTERWARD THE GUESTS TOLD HOW THAT RIOTOUS NIGHT LEFT GREATER WRECKAGE AND MORE VICTIMS THAN THE SIEGE!

AND SO RAOUL AND CLAIR ARE MARRIED AND IT IS REPORTED THAT EVER AFTER THEY LIVED....WELL, AS HAPPILY AS MAY BE EXPECTED OF MARRIED PEOPLE EVERYWHERE.

THEN SIR HUBERT AND HIS GUESTS SPEND AN EXCITING WEEK AT THAT MOST DANGEROUS OF SPORTS; BOAR HUNTING, VAL AND SIR GAWAIN ARE LOATH TO LEAVE, BUT ALL THINGS MUST END.

ON THE DAY OF DEPARTURE SIR HUBERT SHOWS HIS GRATITUDE BY MANY GIFTS.... AND ONCE AGAIN VAL WEARS ON BREAST AND SHIELD HIS FAMILY CREST; THE CRIMSON STALLION.

"SUCH ARE THE REWARDS OF VIRTUE," LAUGHS SIR GAWAIN, "WE CAME IN RAGS AND RIDING CROW-BAIT; WE LEAVE WELL MOUNTED, CLOTHED AND ATTENDED.... AND ALL AT THE PRICE OF A FEW CUTS AND BRUISES!"

HAL FOSTER

LATE AFTERNOON, A SUNNY GLADE; ALL IS PEACE AND BEAUTY, WITH THE EXCEPTION OF TWO AGED KNIGHTS QUARRELING LUSTILY!

NEXT WEEK—The Battle of the Behemoths.

275 5-17-42

**Synopsis:** IN GOOD KING ARTHUR'S DAY LIFE WAS VIOLENT AND THE ONLY GUARANTEE OF CONTINUED EXISTENCE WAS A GOOD SWORD AND THE ABILITY TO USE IT WELL.
ALTHOUGH FIGHTING WAS ALMOST A DAILY OCCURRENCE AMONG THE WARRIORS, NOT EVERY FIGHT WAS A GORY, FATAL AFFAIR.

"NOW, I," SAYS VAL, "ADMIRE THE SHEER NOISINESS OF SIR AVOIRDUPOIS."
"THEN I'LL SECOND THE NOBLE SIR MALNUTRITION," AGREES GAWAIN.

"THIS FUGITIVE FROM NOURISHMENT, THIS SKELETON FROM A FAMILY CLOSET HAS DOUBTED MY VERACITY!" BELLOWS THE FAT KNIGHT TO THE WORLD IN GENERAL.
"I MERELY SAID", THE HAUGHTY ONE EXPLAINS, "THAT HIS BRAINS WERE SO FAT HE WAS UNABLE TO DISTINGUISH BETWEEN TRUTH AND FICTION."

"SUCH LANGUAGE MUST ASSUREDLY LEAD TO VIOLENCE; SHALL WE LEND OUR ASSISTANCE?"

IT IS DIFFICULT TO SEE OUT OF THE PRIMITIVE HELMS OF THAT DISTANT DAY SO..... .....THEY MISSED BY A SCANT EIGHT FEET AND SIR AVOIRDUPOIS CHARGES ON INTO THE WOOD AND GETS LOST.

THE BATTLE IS ON! THEY LACE ON THEIR HELMS BACK TO THE LIMITS OF THE GLADE. THEN, SETTING LANCE AND SHIELD, CHARGE FIERCELY!

BOILING WITH RAGE, THE PLUMP KNIGHT STRIKES AT HIS ENEMY, MISSES, AND FALLS ACROSS HIS SADDLE. HE RECEIVES THREE SMART THUMPS ON THE EAR BEFORE HE REGAINS HIS SEAT.

HIS OPPONENT HAS BETTER LUCK...... AT LEAST HE DID HIT SOMETHING!

VAL BRINGS HIS PRINCIPAL BACK AND HE DISMOUNTS TO CONTINUE THE DUEL.

THE ANVIL CHORUS RINGS OUT, BUT NO DAMAGE IS EVEN POSSIBLE.

DROPPING THEIR SHIELDS, THEY GRASP THEIR SWORDS IN BOTH HANDS FOR ONE GREAT, FATAL STROKE,

HAL FOSTER

BUT THE STROKE NEVER FALLS, THOUGH THE WARRIORS DO..... FROM SHEER WEARINESS!

THE SECONDS REMOVE THE STUFFY, STRAW-PADDED HELMS AND THE TWO GLARE AT EACH OTHER, UNABLE TO SPEAK!

A MOUNTING, SHRILL TUMULT IS HEARD AND DOWN THE TRAIL COME TWO EXCITED DAMES!

NEXT WEEK— "Lady Anne's Night Ride."

276 5-24-42